D1595670

JOURNEYS THROUGH THE MARKET

Travel, Travellers and the Book Trade

PUBLISHING PATHWAYS

JOURNEYS THROUGH THE MARKET
Travel, Travellers and the Book Trade

Edited by
Robin Myers and Michael Harris

ST PAUL'S BIBLIOGRAPHIES

OAK KNOLL PRESS

1999

First published 1999
© 1999 The Contributors

Published in North America by
Oak Knoll Press
310 Delaware Street
New Castle
DE 19720

Published in the United Kingdom by
St Paul's Bibliographies, Ltd.
The Coach House
106 Dover Road
Folkestone
Kent CT20 1NN

Library of Congress Cataloging-in-Publication Data

Journeys through the market : travel, travellers, and the book trade / edited by
Michael Harris and Robin Myers.
      p. cm. -- (Publishing pathways)
    Includes bibliographical references and index.
    ISBN 1-58456-014-2 (USA). -- ISBN 1-873040-56-3 (UK)
    1. Voyages and travels--Great Britain--History--Congresses. 2. Voyages
and travels--Publishing--Great Britain--History--Congresses. 3. Travelers'
wrtings--Publishing--Great Britain--History--Congresses. I. Harris, Michael,
1938- II. Myers, Robin. III. Series.
G242.J68 1999
910.4--dc21
                                                        99-047430

ISBN 1-58456-014-2 (USA)
ISBN 1-873040-56-3 (UK)

Typeset by Ella Whitehead
Printed in England by St Edmundsbury Press, Bury St Edmunds

Contents

Introduction

PRINT AS THE MEDIUM through which the intellectual life of Western Europe was shaped and developed also offered a mechanism for extending public knowledge of the physical world. As ever, commerce and culture combined to powerful effect as the book trade and its customers became involved in a secondary process of exploration. To the book trade travel, crystallised in print, was soon identified as a saleable commodity. The close correspondence in England between commerce and travel gave the published voyages and land journeys to distant places a more than casual interest. As knowledge of the real world was systematically constructed within such large-scale publishing ventures as Hakluyt's *Voyages*, so the experiences of individual travellers and the narratives of specific enterprises extended the possibilities of the genre. Thomas Coryate in the early seventeenth century provided in his eccentric narratives an indication of the more flexible and extra-informational appeal of the travel book – humour, satire and self-revelation included.

As the trade in print diversified and developed at different commercial levels, so the presence of material concerned with travel proliferated. Large compilations and personal narratives were extended during the later seventeenth century by the publication of a variety of small books in which the experience of travel was present. At the same time the content of a growing number of news-based serials kept the public closely informed of the movement of ships and people across the globe. Travel resonated within the output of print and permeated both the national and metropolitan markets. Readers clamoured for the products of the book trade in which information and other more literary elements were sometimes indiscriminately mixed.

Some of the elements of this complex, chronological process are discussed by the contributors to this volume. Anthony Payne, the leading bibliographer of Richard Hakluyt, reveals how his work contributed to the general dissemination of information in print about distant countries at the end of the sixteenth century. He also examines Hakluyt's career and the relationship of his work to that of his European contemporaries as well as subsequent compilers. Michael Harris takes an entirely different line into the subject of travel. Through a detailed reading of the news serials published at the end of the seventeenth century he suggests how their readers were kept informed about the movements of shipping and, in particular, the incidence of shipwreck. Discussion of this form of serial coverage is linked to an investigation into the way in which newspaper reports were related to other forms of shipwreck narrative published in London during the late seventeenth and early eighteenth centuries.

During the course of the eighteenth century the expansion in the output of print ran in tandem with a large increase in the range of direct personal engagement with foreign travel. What had previously been primarily a seriously pragmatic activity – exploration and the opening up of new trade routes – had become, within the more familiar territory of Western Europe, an educational experience. From the seventeenth century onwards members of the families of the ruling élites began to move around established European circuits on what became known as the Grand Tour. By the next century the path between the main urban centres was becoming familiar to whole generations of well-born, though not particularly well-behaved, young Englishmen. Jeremy Black examines this phenomenon and provides a lively picture of a process which was reflected in a variety of forms of printed material. His account of where people went and what happened when they got there gives a dynamic slant to a process which created the first British tourists. Well before 1800 the book trade had begun to explore the possibilities of the growing market for information texts for travellers. Guide books became, by the end of the eighteenth century, one of the staples in the output of some London booksellers and the steeply rising curve of publication was accompanied by an increasing geographical range and specialisation of approach. This is the subject of the review by Giles Barber of the English-language guide books to Europe published before 1870. He suggests how this material related to individual experience during the late eighteenth and early nineteenth centuries and how the London publishers developed new lines to fit the emergent patterns of tourism which accompanied the revolution in communication.

Alongside the populist material published for use, the book trade continued to offer high-price illustrated works designed for the private libraries of the wealthy, and providing, through the most sophisticated techniques of illustration, a form of armchair travel. Charles Newton examines the material generated by interest in the Orient and especially books published in large formats in the first half of the nineteenth century.

Travel was not always a matter of leisure and education. It could and did form part of the life experience of groups and individuals moving across the world to start new lives in the colonies established from the old world. Emigration had its own connections with the cultural world of print. In his fascinating investigation into the reading habits of emigrants to Australia, Bill Bell indicates a pattern of shipboard reading which may surprise those who presume that working-class emigrants, and the majority of 'felons', were illiterate or undesirous of self-improvement.

The conference at which these papers were presented was held at the premises of the Royal Geographical Society, London, and as well as providing access to the unique collections held in the library the Keeper, Andrew Tatham, provided an account of the development of their extensive holdings, which concludes this volume.

Travel and the book trade is a wide-ranging topic but the essays in this volume provide an original view of some of the less-known areas of the subject.

Robin Myers and Michael Harris
June 1999

Contributors

GILES BARBER worked in the Department of Printed Books, Bodleian Library (Oxford) and was Librarian of the Taylor Institution to 1996. He was Panizzi Lecturer at the British Library in 1988 and Sandars Lecturer at the University of Cambridge in 1998 and is past President of the Bibliographical Society. He is currently cataloguing the books and fine bindings from the Rothschild collection at Waddesdon Manor.

BILL BELL is Senior Lecturer in Literature and co-director of the Centre for the History of the Book at the University of Edinburgh. He is general editor, with Jonquil Bevan, of *A History of the Book in Scotland*, to be published in four volumes, and co-editor with Peter Garside of Volume 3 (1800–80). He has written widely on nineteenth-century literature and culture.

JEREMY BLACK is Professor of History at the University of Exeter. His many books include *The British Abroad: The Grand Tour in the 18th century* (1992) and more recently a study of the cultural and political uses of historical maps, *Maps and History: Constructing Images of the Past* (1997).

MICHAEL HARRIS is Senior Lecturer in History in the Faculty of Continuing Education, Birkbeck College and is co-founder, with Robin Myers, of these conferences in book history (from 1979). He has written on various aspects of the history of print, mainly in serial form, and is currently working on a study of the construction and use of news.

CHARLES NEWTON is Deputy Head of the collection of designs in the Department of Prints, Drawings and Paintings at the Victoria and Albert Museum. He has special responsibility for the Searight Collection of images of the Middle East.

ANTHONY PAYNE is a Director of the London antiquarian booksellers Bernard Quaritch Ltd and Honorary Secretary of the Hakluyt Society. His Hakluyt Society lecture *Richard Hakluyt and His Books*, published in 1997, includes an interim census (compiled with P. A. Neville-Sington) of surviving copies of Hakluyt's *Divers Voyages* and *Pricipal Navigations*.

ANDREW TATHAM is Keeper at the Royal Geographical Society (with the Institute of British Geographers). He is Head of Information Resources at the Royal Geographical Society and has written extensively on tactile mapping. He is President of the British Cartographic Society.

List of Participants

Myriam Altamirano
Biochemist, Medical Research Council, Cambridge

Sarah Anderson
Founder of the Travel Bookshop and writer

Laurel Brake
Lecturer, FCE, Birkbeck College

Andrew Cook
Archivist, India Office Records, British Library

Angela Craft
Book conservator and historian of the book

Robert Cross
Publisher, St Paul's Bibliographies

Timothy Cutts
Assistant librarian, National Library of Wales

Carlo Dumontet
National Art Library, Victoria & Albert Museum

John Eade
Reader in Anthropology & Sociology, Roehampton Institute, London

Judy Edwards
Researcher

Alexander Fyjis-Walker
Publisher of travel guides

Amy Flanders
MA student, Centre for English Studies, University of London

Richard Ford
Antiquarian bookseller

Angus Fraser
Researcher

Julie Gregory
MA student, History of the Book, School of Advanced Studies, University of London

Angel Gurria
PhD student, Emmanuel College, Cambridge

Elizabeth Hagglund
PhD student (English Department) University of Birmingham

David J. Hall
Deputy Librarian, University of Cambridge

Julie Harvey
Entomology Librarian, Natural History Museum, London

Jessica Haynes
British Library

John Hewish
British Library

Sheila Hingley
Librarian, Canterbury Cathedral Library

A. W. Huish
Retired librarian

Oliver Irvine
Specialist, Books and Manuscript Department, Christie's

Philip Henry Jones
Lecturer, Department of Information and Library Studies, University of Wales, Aberystwyth

Colin Lee
Book collector

Yvonne Lewis
Assistant libraries adviser, National Trust

Giles Mandelbrote
Curator, British Library

G. R. Marvin

Miriam Miller
Computer consultant

Martha Norrbach
MA student, History of the Book and PhD student, University of Helsinki

Margaret Payne
Librarian

Michael Perkin
Reading University Library (part-time)

Penelope Rudd
Bookseller (travel books)

Marja Smolenaars
Sir Thomas Browne Institute, University of Leiden

Ann Sproat
Special collections librarian, Courtauld Institute of Art

Carl Thompson
DPhil student (voyages and travels and the Romantic imaginations), Pembroke College, Oxford

Jean Tsushima
Archivist emeritus, Honourable Artillery Company

Patricia Usick
Egyptologist

Ann Veenhoff
Sir Thomas Browne Institute, University of Leiden

Walker, A.

John Walwyn Jones
Bookseller, Questor Books

Marion Wattman
Researcher

Veronica Watts
Antiquarian bookseller

David Wickham
Archivist, Clothworkers' Company

Ian Willison
Centre for English Studies, University of London

David Wills
History teacher and PhD student in travel writing, Roehampton Institute

'Strange, remote, and farre distant countreys': the travel books of Richard Hakluyt

ANTHONY PAYNE

Note: *Numbers in* **bold type** *refer to the checklist of Hakluyt's books printed at the end of this paper*

IN 1552, THE YEAR OF Richard Hakluyt's birth, the Spanish historian Francisco López de Gómara wrote, 'The greatest event since the creation of the world (excluding the incarnation of Him who created it) is the discovery of the Indies'. This was echoed two hundred years later by Adam Smith in the *Wealth of Nations*: 'the discovery of America, and that of a passage to the East Indies by the Cape of Good Hope, are the two greatest and most important events recorded in the history of mankind'.[1] The theme of this paper is how (in Hakluyt's words) knowledge of the 'strange, remote, and farre distant countreys'[2] beyond Europe was disseminated in printed form, in particular through the books of Richard Hakluyt.

Hakluyt's major work, the *Principal Navigations, Voiages ... and Discoveries of the English Nation* (first edition 1589, **11**; second edition, considerably revised and enlarged, 1598–1600, **16**), is cited by numerous bibliographies, which generally concur that it is 'difficult to overrate the importance and value of this extraordinary collection of voyages'.[3] However, reiterating the book's iconic status does not necessarily explain its nature or achievement, while the frequent, uncritical, quotation of Froude's appellation of it as 'the prose epic of the modern English nation'[4] imposes a Victorian frame of reference on to a sixteenth-century work that does little to aid its understanding within its contemporary context. Froude, in reviewing the Hakluyt Society's early publications and castigating what he believed was the Society's failure to reprint the 'heroic tales' found in the *Principal Navigations*, argued:

What the old epics were to the royally or nobly born, this modern epic is to the common people.... We can conceive nothing, not the songs of Homer himself, which would be read, among us at least, with more enthusiastic interest than these plain massive tales; and a people's edition of them in these days, when the writings

1

of Ainsworth and Eugène Sue circulate in tens of thousands, would perhaps be the most blessed antidote which could be bestowed upon us. The heroes themselves were the men of the people – the Joneses, the Smiths, the Davises, the Drakes; and no courtly pen, with the one exception of Raleigh, lent its polish or its varnish to set them off.[5]

Froude's remarks, uttered in 1852, offer an interesting glimpse of a particular strand of mid-nineteenth-century imperial thinking, but this should not be read back into Hakluyt's own time.

Here I would like to suggest various approaches to Hakluyt's books under a number of interrelated headings – his patronage and connections; Italian and French influences; his use of illustration and his presentation of texts; his intentions; and, finally, his impact and readership – in an attempt to form a rounded appreciation of his work and the nature of his achievement. I hope to indicate that Hakluyt's part in the publication of over 25 travel books marks a contribution to travel literature far beyond the mere chronicling of English voyages as a prodrome to empire. It should be stressed, however, that I am not prescribing a 'correct' reading of Hakluyt, only sketching various possible approaches to his texts.

Patronage and connections
The son of a member of the Company of Skinners, who came from an old Herefordshire family, Hakluyt was educated at Westminster School.[6] As a boy he visited his cousin and namesake, Richard Hakluyt the elder, a lawyer at the Middle Temple, who, responding to the young Hakluyt's curiosity about 'certeine books of cosmographie' and a 'universall mappe' lying open on the table, spoke to him of the 'seas, gulfs, bayes ... empires ... and territories' of each part of the earth, of 'their special commodities, & particular wants, which by the benefit of traffike, & intercourse of merchants, are plentifully supplied'. From the map, his cousin brought him to a Bible and directed him to Psalm 107, 'where I read, that they which go downe to the sea in ships, and occupy by the great waters, they see the works of the Lord, and his woonders in the deepe, &c. Which words of the Prophet together with my cousin's discourse (things of high and rare delight to my young nature) tooke in me so deepe an impression, that I constantly resolved, if ever I were preferred to the University ... would by Gods assistance prosecute that knowledge and kinde of literature'[7] (this, and much else of what we know about Hakluyt's biography, is to be found in the prefatory matter to the two editions of the *Principal Navigations*). He kept to this resolution and in 1570 went up to Oxford, entering Christ Church, at that time a major centre for the

study of descriptive geography.[8] There Hakluyt 'by degrees read over whatsoever printed or written discoveries and voyages' he found extant 'in Greeke, Latine, Italian, Spanish, Portugall, French, or English' and, later, lectured on geography.[9]

Hakluyt had developed a sustained and deep interest in geography and travel by his late 20s; at some stage (the exact date is uncertain) he was ordained as a priest in the Church of England. He was well connected and enjoyed the financial support, through exhibitions while at Oxford, of the Skinners' and, notably, the Clothworkers' Companies.[10] Prominent among the Clothworkers was Thomas Staper (elected Master in 1590), who was thanked by Hakluyt in the preface to the first edition of the *Principall Navigations* for furnishing 'divers thinges touching the trade of Turkie, and other places in the East' (the 'speciall industrie' of Staper and others in 'the happy renuing' of the Levant trade was noted in the second edition).[11] It has been suggested that Hakluyt's debt to the Clothworkers, who, at the request of the Lord Treasurer, Lord Burghley, continued to grant a 'pension' to him after he was appointed to the embassy in Paris in 1583, explains the deft weighting of the *Principal Navigations* in favour of the long-range trades associated with the Clothworkers' Company, playing down the short-range traffic to North-West Europe of the Company of Merchants Adventurers.[12] While the Merchants Adventurers do not feature at all in the first edition and as something of a historical curiosity only in the second, Hakluyt clearly states in his prefatory address to the 'favourable reader' in the first edition that his coverage excluded all voyages close to home and not of discovery.[13] The book's supposed bias against one trading interest may be due, therefore, as much to Hakluyt's geographical criteria for inclusion as to the source of his patronage. Moreover, Hakluyt's use of contacts with London business-men should not be exaggerated, for Staper was not at all representative of City merchants and Hakluyt does not seem to have taken advantage of opportunities to introduce himself to City men with ordinary trading interests.[14]

By the early 1580s Hakluyt was known to the Secretary of State, Sir Francis Walsingham (an associate of Hakluyt the elder), Sir Francis Drake, Sir Humphrey Gilbert, Walter Ralegh (to whom Hakluyt was to dedicate his editions of Peter Martyr and Laudonnière, **8, 9**) and others who were active in promoting overseas ventures. In 1584 he was granted an audience with the Queen, at which he presented her with his manuscript *Discourse of Western Planting* (**3**, the Queen's copy is lost and the sole extant version is a scrivener's copy, probably made in 1585, perhaps intended for Walsingham, and now in the New York Public Library).[15] Dedicated to the Queen, the *Discourse* elaborates ambitious colonial projects in North America and opportunities to undermine the Spanish American empire, policies associated with Ralegh and his circle. It is untypical of Hakluyt's *œuvre* as a whole, being a sustained prose work in his own words and intended not for general publication in printed form, but, circulated in manuscript only, to promote the interests of a particular faction at court. It was also, perhaps as significantly, designed to further Hakluyt's own interests in obtaining patronage and was presented to the Queen along with an autograph manuscript of his '*Analysis*' of Aristotle's *Politics* (BL Royal MS 12 G. XIII), which 'supplied the political and moral context within which he expected Elizabeth and her counsellors (all trained and many, like Sir William Cecil and Elizabeth herself, very much committed humanists) to judge his proposals for English colonization'. Although it has been called the 'greatest of all Elizabethan colonial tracts',[16] the *Discourse* had no discernible political influence, but whether the text was really intended to be read, and to exert reasoned influence thereby, is worth pondering. Rather, might the book be best seen as a physical emblem of Hakluyt's learning, of his sagacious counsel, an element in the complex ritual of posturing and self-promotion characteristic of the quest for courtly patronage in Renaissance Europe? A thoughtful examination of the text leads one recent reviewer to conclude that the *Discourse* 'emerges as a strikingly inconsistent creation, combining accurate information and shrewd assessment with wild overstatement and rhetorical flights of fancy',[17] but this, maybe, subjects it to a scrutiny of a closeness unlikely to have been made in Hakluyt's own time.

The first of many printed books associated with Hakluyt, John Florio's translation, undertaken with Hakluyt's encouragement and at his expense, of Cartier's *Shorte and Briefe Narration* of his travels in North America, appeared in 1580 (1, I will return to this later). Two years later Hakluyt published his first own book, *Divers Voyages touching the Discoverie of America* (2), without his name on the title-page, but with a dedication initialled 'R. H.' to Philip Sidney, a Christ Church contemporary (and later Walsingham's son-in-law), 'trusting also that your worshippe will continue & increase your accustomed favour towarde these godly and honourable discoveries' and drawing attention to the 'great conquest and plantings of the Spaniards & Portingales' in America. He expressed the hope 'that the time approcheth … that we of England may share and part stakes (if we will ourselves) both with the

Spaniarde and the Portingale in part of America, and other regions as yet undiscovered'.[18] A collection of informative material for prospective colonisation projects in North America, the *Divers Voyages* was licensed on 21 May 1582.[19] At least one reader seems to have been influenced (or was confirmed in his opinions) by it, for the next day a copy was bought by Sir Edmund Brudenell, who, soon afterwards, signed up to join Gilbert's colonising project (inscribed by Brudenell, this is now in the Free Library of Philadelphia, one of only 22 recorded surviving copies).[20] The major land-grants for participants in the enterprise took place in June, so it has been suggested that the appearance of Hakluyt's book was the signal for Gilbert and his associates to take up the pursuit of subscribers in a major way.[21] Sidney, who invested in July, later remarked in a letter to Sir Edward Stafford that he 'was hauff perswaded to enter into the journey of Sir Humphry Gilbert very eagerli; whereunto your Mr Hackluit hath served for a very good trumpet'.[22]

In June 1582 Hakluyt himself contemplated following Sir Humphrey Gilbert across the Atlantic to America, as is evident from a letter of 6 August 1583 sent to Hakluyt from Newfoundland ('You thought in June last to have followed us your selfe')[23] by Stephen Parmenius, his Hungarian-born Oxford room-mate, who composed an epic rendering in verse of Gilbert's enterprise, *De navigatione ... Humfredi Gilberti ... carmen* (1582, reprinted in both editions of the *Principal Navigations*).[24] Instead, in 1583, he took up the post of chaplain-secretary to Sir Edward Stafford, the English ambassador in Paris, an appointment he was to hold until 1588. In France he gathered intelligence for Walsingham, whose patronage was increasingly important, as reflected in the first edition of the *Principall Navigations* which was not only dedicated to Walsingham but was also licensed for publication by him.[25] It is possible that the late inclusion of the narrative of Drake's 'famous voyage' round the world was due to Walsingham, anxious to maintain close control of information concerning a venture that, although a source of national pride and great profit (not least to the Queen and to Walsingham himself as one of its original backers) had always been politically sensitive, initially in terms of international relations and, since the summer of 1589, because Drake was in official disgrace after the failure of his Portuguese expedition. Printed on twelve unnumbered pages the narrative is found inserted in most, but not all, copies. It is generally agreed that it cannot have been ready when printing of the book itself was completed, but beyond this, its dating remains controversial. Drake's latest biographer, Harry Kelsey, argues that it was composed after 1595, possibly in 1596, which would rule out

Walsingham's involvement as he died in 1590. Kelsey's historical and textual reasons for suggesting a late composition are certainly plausible. He also contends that the Drake leaves cannot have been printed at almost the same time as the original book, since in each of the 'many copies' inspected by him they are 'obviously inserted after the edges were trimmed for binding, after vermin had eaten holes in the paper, and/or after the facing pages were otherwise stained or marred'.[26] However, while condition is useful in establishing in particular instances that the leaves have been added at a much later date (as is undoubtedly often the case), such deterioration is generally improbable in copies to which they were added only five years or so later. Kelsey's observation about trimming is not conclusive in establishing when the leaves were inserted in particular copies: trimming could equally well have occurred within a few weeks or months as five years after the book's first publication. A detailed survey of over 50 copies, including an examination of the paper and typography, concludes that 'the Drake leaves could have been produced to match the rest of the book at any time within five or ten years after 1589'.[27] In this instance, then, the bibliographical evidence is simply not exact enough to be of positive assistance to the historian in reconstructing events.

Hakluyt's was the first detailed narrative of Drake's 'famous voyage' to appear in print, many years after the events it describes, but Walsingham himself must have been aware of the limitations of his control over information, for Sir Edward Stafford had informed him from the embassy in Paris in October 1584: 'I find from Mr Haklitt that Drake's journey is kept very secret in England, but here it is in everyone's mouth. When questioned about it, I have answered as an ignorant body, as indeed I am, except for what I find by their speeches here'.[28] The French, indeed, seem to have had remarkably good information: the botanist Charles de L'Ecluse had visited England and obtained botanical specimens collected on the voyage, publishing an account of them in 1582, while the historian Lancelot Voisin, sieur de La Popelinière, is our source for the Queen's retention of Drake's records of the voyage in order to prevent publication. A richly decorated chart was sent to Henry of Navarre (later King of France) in response to his request to Walsingham in 1585 for material on the voyage.[29] The circumstances of Hakluyt's printing of Drake's circumnavigation might, therefore, lie more in Drake's relationship with the Queen than in a carefully pursued policy of official secrecy. All that can be said for certain is that Hakluyt made clear in his preface to the 1589 *Principall Navigations* that although he had intended to include an account of Drake's exploit, he had 'yeelded unto those my freindes which pressed me in the matter' and not done so to avoid anticipating 'another mans paines and charge in drawing all the services of that worthie Knight into one volume'.[30] In the event this 'one volume' was not forthcoming, so it is natural that Hakluyt attempted subsequently to fill the gap by printing a notice of the 'famous voyage' for insertion in his own book.

Walsingham, or other government officials, may have been responsible for the changes in the account of the Bowes embassy to Ivan the Terrible, which commences on p.491 and occurs in either of two states in the 1589 *Principall Navigations*. The original, in the first-hand, is headed 'The Ambassage of Sir Hierome Bowes to the Emperour of Moscovie 1583', the second, in the third-hand, is headed 'A Briefe Discourse of the Voyage of Sir Jerome Bowes ... printed this second time'. This substitution is usually thought to have occurred at the behest of the Muscovy Company, fearful that Bowes's narrative might be prejudicial to its future dealings with the Tsar.[31] It is certainly true that the Muscovy Company could exert such pressure. It complained to the Lord Treasurer, Lord Burghley, that certain passages in Giles Fletcher's *Of the Russe Common Wealth* (1591) might cause offence to the detriment of the Company's position in Russia and successfully obtained the government's suppression of the book.[32] The Bowes account 'printed this second time' is shorter and less immediate, but it also lists in some detail concessions obtained from Ivan by the ambassador 'for the behoofe of the merchants', such as 'that all strangers were forbidden to trade any more into Russia, and that the passage and trade to all the Emperors northren coasts and countries, from the Ward house to the River of Ob should be onely free to the English nation' and 'the abatement of all theyre custome'.[33] At a time of ongoing negotiations with Ivan's successor, Theodor, the Muscovy Company was keen to maintain its privileges[34] and a recitation of those previously obtained would do no harm, not so much for a putative Russian as for an English audience, because diplomatic negotiations were, of course, conducted by the Queen's ambassadors, not by the Company. Might, therefore, Hakluyt have simply been handed the alternative, and in some respects more useful, account by the Muscovy Company and obliged by printing it, rather than being subject to a quasi-censorship of his material?

One more figure to note in the genesis of the *Principall Navigations* is the courtier, poet, dabbler in alchemy, investor in Frobisher's voyages and friend of Sidney, Sir Edward Dyer, who is singled out for exceptional gratitude in Hakluyt's acknowledgements: 'In respect of a generall incouragement in this laborious travaile, it were grosse ingratitude in mee to forget that man, whose onely name doth carrie with it sufficient estimation and love, and that is Master Edward Dier'.[35] Interestingly, Dyer had played an important role in publishing John Dee's *General and Rare Memorials pertayning to the perfect arte of navigation* (1577), in which he is praised in the dedicatory verses as 'That Redy freend'.[36] This was the only part printed of a projected large treatise on all aspects of navigation, naval power and sovereignty, which was to have included a compendium of voyages as its final part (the unpublished manuscript of the latter, 'Of Famous and Rich Discoveries', survives in BL Cotton MS Vitellius C. VII).[37] Dee's account of King Edgar's voyage in *General and Rare Memorials* was reprinted by Hakluyt in the 1589 *Principall Navigations* and there are references to Dee in both editions of the *Principal Navigations*, but despite their shared interest in collecting voyages and their shared friendship with Dyer, I am unaware of a documented instance of the two meeting, although Dee's dealings with the elder Hakluyt, Sidney, Walsingham, Ralegh, the Gilbert brothers and other associates of Hakluyt are recorded.[38]

After Walsingham's death, in the feuding political world of the final decade of Elizabeth's reign, Hakluyt seems increasingly to have placed himself in the orbit of Sir Robert Cecil, Secretary of State from 1596 until 1608, to whom he dedicated the second and third volumes of the second edition of the *Principal Navigations*. It is evident from the closing paragraphs of the 1599 dedication that Cecil had been especially active on Hakluyt's behalf: 'I cannot but acknowledge my selfe much indebted for your favourable letters heretofore written in my behalfe in mine honest causes.... I may adde, that when this worke was to passe unto the presse, your honour ... with extraordinarie commendation did approve and allow my labours, and desire to publish the same'.[39] Hakluyt describes himself in the dedication to Cecil of his translation of Galvão's *Discoveries of the World* (1601, 19) as 'Your Honors Chaplein', while Cecil's patronage was important in lobbying for ecclesiastical preferment for Hakluyt, who was installed as a prebendary of Westminster Abbey in 1602 and held various offices there until his death in 1616.[40]

It is possible that Hakluyt's indebtedness to Cecil lies behind the suppression of the 'Cadiz leaves' in the first volume of the *Principal Navigations* (1598, pp.607-19). These leaves recount the 1596 raid on Cadiz in which Cecil's inveterate rival, the Earl of Essex, played a prominent role, and Hakluyt himself may have withdrawn them out of prudent considerations of patronage, an act of 'self censorship' rather than compulsion by orders from above. (The volume was re-issued with a new title-page, dated 1599, omitting reference to this 'famous victorie', but no correlation is apparent from surviving copies between the date of the title-page and the presence or not of the Cadiz leaves.) Although a well-known example of Elizabethan censorship this incident has not been explained conclusively, and such censorship as there was must have been laxly implemented because the offending leaves survive in a large number of copies.[41] It is certainly misleading to say that it was ordered by the Queen because of Essex's fall from her favour, since the political chronology of the Earl's decline cannot be readily reconciled with the date of the book's publication: to say that Essex had 'fallen' in 1599, the year of the supposed censorship of the Cadiz leaves, is to read back into that year the events leading to his rebellion and execution in 1601.[42] Moreover, despite his dramatic end as a traitor, his reputation did not wane irrevocably and even his political enemies, Cecil and Nottingham, admitted that the Earl had died a Christian. A reaction in Essex's favour set in, which promoted the survival of the radical attitudes and policies (including the anti-Spanish Protestant crusade) associated with him. The Cadiz raid still carried great weight many years later and Hakluyt's narrative was printed again in *Purchas his Pilgrimes* (28) in 1625, the year in which the Duke of Buckingham ordered another attack on Cadiz, an action inspired by memories of 1596.[43]

Apart from exclusively Essex-related interpretations fitting awk-wardly with the chronology of the Earl's demise, the problem of any explanation related directly to him is that it is difficult to read the Cadiz narrative itself as overtly partisan. There is no explicit documentary evidence for official censorship, although a prohibition on the publication of accounts of the raid had been issued in 1596, principally, it seems, due to rivalries at court and to quell squabbling amongst the rival commanders.[44] It is clear that Hakluyt himself was not attempting to promote the cause of Essex in printing the Cadiz narrative, for the volume is dedicated to Charles Howard, Earl of Nottingham, who, as Lord Admiral, had also played a leading part in the raid and was, moreover, no friend of Essex.[45] Hakluyt writes in his dedication:

As for the late renoued expedition and honourable voyage to Cadiz ... because they be hereafter so judicially set downe, by ... an eye witnesse in all that action, I referre your good L. to his faithfull report, wherein I trust (as much as in him lay) he hath wittingly deprived no man of his right.[46]

The narrative itself, based on the eye-witness account of Roger Marbeck[47] (unnamed by Hakluyt), a physician who accompanied the Lord Admiral, opens by giving equal prominence to Howard and Essex, 'the two most noble and renowned Lords Generals: the L. Robert Earle of Essex, and the L. Charles Howard L. High Admiral of England'. It is unlikely that Hakluyt would have printed a text that could be construed as partial, intentionally or otherwise, to Essex in a book dedicated to one of Essex's rivals. Indeed partisanship seems not to have occurred to Hakluyt at all. His prefatory remarks in this volume suggest that his motive was simply to publish a good story to the credit of all concerned and of the nation as a whole: an 'excellent discourse' on the Spanish Armada and another on the

expedition to Cadiz under the two of the most noble and valiant peeres of the realme, I meane, the renoumed Erle of Essex, and the right honorable the Lord Charles Howard, Lord high Admirall of England, made 1596 unto the strong citie of Cadiz, I have set downe as a double epiphonema to conclude this my first volume withall.[48]

Cecil was, however, becoming increasingly ascendant, as were his pacific policies towards Spain, and a downplaying of the Cadiz expedition which was closely, if not exclusively, associated with Cecil's principal political rival would have done Hakluyt no harm, especially if he expected Cecil's intercession in obtaining promotion in the Church. Hakluyt, it may be suggested, therefore withdrew the Cadiz leaves voluntarily out of deference to his patron, because the shifting emphasis in foreign policy made politic a distancing from the Cadiz raid and the bellicose anti-Spanish stance it represented. As a final reflection, it is conceivable that Nottingham (Howard) may have been instrumental in the suppression, or that Hakluyt was acting out of deference to him as the dedicatee of the first volume. In any event, Nottingham and Cecil were as one: as a contemporary observed, the Lord Admiral would 'do nothing, but what stands with Mr Secretary's liking', while Cecil was increasingly favoured by the Queen, 'soe carefull he is of her busines and service. And indeed the whole waight of the state lies upon hym'.[49]

After these admittedly rather involved matters, it may be mentioned that the Cadiz raid has another bibliographical aspect: books were an especially popular form of plunder, including several looted from the Jesuit College at Cadiz by Edward Doughtie, which are now in Hereford Cathedral library, and many from the episcopal library at Faro (raided on the voyage home), given in 1600 by Essex to Sir Thomas Bodley's new library at Oxford.[50]

In the early years of the seventeenth century Hakluyt was engaged as an adviser to the newly formed East India Company and was an investor in the Virginia Company, both connections reflected in the various books associated with him published during this period.[51] These include *The Journall of Jacob Corneliszen Neck* (1601, 20), translated 'by the perswasion of M. Richard Hakluyt' and dedicated to Sir Thomas Smith, Governor of the East India Company, for the guidance of 'your East Indie voyage', *Virginia Richly Valued* (1609, 21), dedicated by Hakluyt to the 'Counsellors, and others the cheerefull adventurors for the advancement of that Christian and noble plantation in Virginia' as a work that 'doth yeeld much light to our enterprise now on foot',[52] Lescarbot's *Nova Francia: or the description of that part of New France, which is one continent with Virginia* (1609, 22), translated by Pierre Erondelle, who states that the French original 'was brought to me to be translated by M. Richard Hakluyt ... and by him this part was selected and chosen ... for the particular use of this nation, to the end that comparing the goodness of the lands of the northern parts herein mentioned with that of Virginia ... may be given to prosecute that generous and goodly action',[53] and Gothard's *Dialogues in the English and Malaiane Languages ... now faithfully translated into English tongue ... for their sakes, who happily shall hereafter undertake a voyage to the East-Indies* (1614, 25). The last had been drawn to the East India Company's attention by Hakluyt,[54] was translated by him from the Latin edition, and revised by Augustine Spalding, who had first gone out to Bantam in 1601[55] and who dedicated the book to Sir Thomas Smith, Governor of the East India Company.

Hakluyt died in 1616 and is buried in Westminster Abbey. The outline of his life, patronage and career is straightforward: gentry background, Oxford and ordination, government connections, the patronage of leading political figures, a concern with colonial developments, including a personal involvement in some of the new joint-stock ventures of the early seventeenth century.

Italian and French influences

Most notable of the early literary influences on Hakluyt was Italian – Ramusio's *Navigationi* (1550–59), the most systematic collection of voyages of the period and a great improvement in organisational rigour on the efforts of his predecessors.[56] The *Navigationi* was 'the first published collection of historical documents other than collections of laws and decretals; the first large and planned collection of travel documents, and therefore the first approach to the concept of a documented history of travel and geography'.[57] Many of Ramusio's texts were printed for the first time, among them, for example, the history of Africa by Leo Africanus, later published in English, with Hakluyt's approbation, in 1600 (18). Marco Antonio Pigafetta, a Venetian resident in London, publication of whose *Itinerario* (1585, 4) was exhorted by Hakluyt, later contributed a commendatory verse to the 1589 *Principall Navigations* in which Hakluyt was compared to Ramusio,[58] a supreme accolade for Hakluyt and indicative of the esteem in which Ramusio was held at the time.

Hakluyt learnt Italian and obtained a set of Ramusio at Oxford some time in the 1570s. The very first book that he was involved with, Cartier's *Shorte and Briefe Narration of ... discoveries ... called Newe France* (1580, 1), was translated at his expense and from his copy of Ramusio by John Florio, then teaching Italian at Oxford[59] and famous later for his *A Worlde of Wordes, or ... Dictionarie in Italian and English* (1598) and his translation of Montaigne's *Essayes* into English (1603). Florio's prefatory address to the reader, specifically 'Gentlemen, merchants, and pilots', states that he undertook the translation

for the benefite and behoofe of those that shall attempt any newe discoverie in the northweast partes of America ... here is the description of a countrey no lesse fruitful and pleasant in al respects than is England, Fraunce, or Germany ... but three weekes sayling from Bristowe.... Al which opportunities beside manye others, mighte suffice to induce oure Englishmen, not onely to fall to some traffique wyth the inhabitants, but also to plant a colonie in some convenient place, and so to possesse the countrey without the gainsaying of any man, whiche was the judgement and counsell of John Baptista Ramusius, a learned and excellent cosmographer, & secretary to the famous state of Venice.[60]

Hakluyt's role in the publication of the translation is not indicated by Florio, but the evidence for his involvement is found in the dedication to Philip Sidney of *Divers Voyages* (1582, 2), where Hakluyt states, 'at my charges, and other of my friendes by my exhortation, I caused Jacques Cartiers two voyages ... to bee translated out of my volumes, which are to be annexed to this'.[61] 'Annexed to this' apparently indicates Hakluyt's intention that the Cartier could be added to the *Divers Voyages*, but only one copy survives so bound, at St John's College, Oxford, with the contemporary binding instruction to include 'Florio ... iind' (this is in a contemporary vellum binding stamped 'P S', but, although tempting, it cannot be established as once belonging to Philip Sidney).[62]

Hakluyt's intention in publishing Cartier might have been to publicise the colonial opportunities of the St Lawrence region in support of Edward Cotton's expedition there in 1580, but I think that the book's Italian ancestry is more striking and pertinent to bibliographical history. From the printing of the Columbus letters in 1493, Italy was the most important clearing house for the receipt and spread throughout Europe of information about the West's encounter with the peoples and lands of the wider world. Hakluyt's immediate precursor as collector of travel narratives in English, Richard Willes, a renegade Jesuit, had spent much time in Italy, where he met the Jesuits' historian of their overseas enterprises, Giovanni Pietro Maffei. The extensive accounts of China and Japan printed for the first time in English by Richard Willes in his *History of Travayle in the West and East Indies* (1577) relied entirely upon materials sent to Rome from Jesuits working in the East, while his book also included the first English translation of the Italian Varthema's travels, an especially important account of the Middle East.[63]

Moving on from Italian influences on Hakluyt, we can now turn to Hakluyt's time in France.[64] Here he was able to gather much information and develop his geographical interests, not just from French sources but also Portuguese, from Dom Antonio, the exiled claimant to the Portuguese throne who, 'with five or six of his best captaynes and pilots, one of whom was borne in East India', was consulted personally by Hakluyt.[65] He became acquainted with the French royal cosmographer, André Thevet,[66] who lent him the manuscript of Laudonnière's *L'Histoire notable de la Floride*, published in France with Hakluyt's assistance in 1586 (and the next year in an English translation by Hakluyt himself, 5, 9), as he noted in the dedication to the second volume of the *Principal Navigations* (1599): 'I had caused the foure voyages of Ribault, Laudonniere, and Gourges to Florida, at mine owne charges to be printed in Paris, which by the malice of some too much affectioned to the Spanish faction, had bene above twentie yeeres suppressed'.[67] Thevet complained that it had been published without his permission, but relations between the two do not seem to have been permanently broken, for Hakluyt subsequently obtained the Codex Mendoza from Thevet.[68] This magnificent Aztec pictographic manuscript, produced in 1541–2 at the behest of the Viceroy of New Spain, Don Antonio de Mendoza, for presentation to the Emperor Charles V, had been captured *en route* from Mexico by French pirates and was in Thevet's hands by 1553. It passed, with Hakluyt's other papers, to Samuel Purchas, who reproduced its pictograms in *Purchas his Pilgrimes* (1625, **28**), and then to John Selden, after whose death (1654) it was acquired, along with the bulk of Selden's library, by the Bodleian, Oxford.[69] Also in France Hakluyt obtained Espejo's travels in New Mexico,[70] included in the 1586 Madrid edition of González de Mendoza's account of China, and had it printed, in Spanish, at his own expense in Paris in the same year (**6**). Only one copy of Hakluyt's printing survives, given in 1590 to Thomas Harriot by John Dee and now in the British Library.[71] (Hakluyt does not seem to have been involved in an English translation of Espejo's narrative, published in 1587 as *New Mexico. Otherwise, the voiage of Anthony de Espejo ... Translated out of the Spanish copie printed first at Madreel, 1586, and afterward at Paris in the same yeare*).[72] The greatest editorial achievement to stem from Hakluyt's years in Paris was his edition (in the original Latin) of Peter Martyr's history of Spain in the New World (1587, **8**). Based on the most complete text, printed only once before, in 1530, it was subsequently used by Michael Lok in publishing the first complete edition in English (and, indeed, in any vernacular language), *De Novo Orbe, or the Historie of the West Indies* (1612, **24**).[73]

González de Mendoza appeared in English as *The Historie of the Great and Mightie Kingdome of China* in 1588 (**10**), with Hakluyt's encouragement acknowledged by the translator, Robert Parke. It was taken from the 1586 Madrid text – the fullest, and the one that included Espejo's New Mexico.[74] Hakluyt was aware of the textual superiority of the Madrid edition over the 1585 Rome original, but until the meticulous bibliographical examinations of Wagner and Retana[75] in the early twentieth century, the differences between the two editions were often unrecognised. For example, the editors of the Hakluyt Society's reprint of Parke's 1588 translation did not realise that it derived from the Madrid edition, nor that the Madrid text differed from the Rome original, so that when they collated the English translation against the Rome version they could only express puzzlement about the origins of the additional material.[76] The printer of the English González de Mendoza was John Wolfe,[77] an entrepreneurial, if controversial, figure, who also published English editions of Meierus's *Instructions* for travellers (1589, **12**), Lopes's *Congo* (1597, **15**) and Linschoten's *Discours of Voyages* (1598, **17**), in all of which Hakluyt was involved as an encourager or intermediary.

Illustration and text

The Lopes and Linschoten are the only substantially illustrated books associated with Hakluyt to be published in England. This may reflect the lack of competent engravers in England, but the expense of engraving may have been as important (more needs to be known about the financing of Hakluyt's publications, but he seems to have borne most of the costs). His three voyage collections include maps, but the two in the *Divers Voyages* are somewhat extempore, while in both editions of the *Principal Navigations* Hakluyt displays no great concern with this aspect of illustration. For the 1589 edition, while readily admitting the usefulness of maps to the reader, he contented himself, as he stated in his preface, 'with inserting into the worke one of the best generall mappes of the world onely'[78] (it was a copy of the standard Ortelius world map first published in 1570, revised in 1587), because of the anticipated appearance of Molyneux's 'very large and most exact terrestrial globe'. The highly important world map on Mercator's projection (usually ascribed to Edward Wright and derived from Molyneux's globe) associated with the second edition of the *Principal Navigations* is found in under ten per cent of the extant copies recorded by the Census, which, combined with the absence of any reference to it in the book's dedications or prefaces, suggests that the book was available with or without the map, or, as likely, that it was not necessarily intended for publication with the book.[79] R. A. Skelton has written of Hakluyt's attitude to maps:

Even if his [Hakluyt's] geographical interests tended to lie at the periphery of knowledge, where cartographers had recourse to hypothesis and conjecture, this may suggest no very regular recourse to maps or lively confidence in their information. Indirectly, indeed, Hakluyt frequently writes as if a map or a globe were on his table or in his mind's eye.... But we do not often have the impression so forcibly conveyed in the writings of Dee or Ralegh and in the collections of Lord Burghley, that he is positively thinking in a cartographic idiom.... It is perhaps significant that in the *Principal Navigations* only textual extracts are printed from the wall maps of Sebastian Cabot ... and of Mercator.[80]

The two major illustrated books associated with Hakluyt are the first two parts of Theodore de Bry's collection of voyages, *America*, both published in Frankfurt. In the first part, Harriott's *A Briefe and True Report of the New Found Land of Virginia* (1590, **13**),[81] de Bry published for the first time a series of engravings after drawings by John White,[82] with commentaries translated by Hakluyt and with its own title-page, *The true pictures and fashions of the people in that parte of America now called*

Virginia ... Translated out of Latin into English by Richard Hackluit. Diligentlye collected and draowne by Ihon White who was sent thiter speciallye and for the same purpose by ... Sir Walter Ralegh ... now cutt in copper and first published by Theodore de Bry. In his address 'to the gentle reader' prefacing this section, de Bry says that he was able to 'offer unto you the true pictures ... wich by the helpe of Maister Richard Hakluyt of Oxford Minister of God's Word, who first encouraged me to publish the worke, I creaved out of the verye original of Maister Ihon White an English paynter who was sent into the countrye to describe the shapes of the inhabitants'.

The preface of the second part of *America*, Le Moyne's *Brevis narratio eorum quae in Florida Americae provincia Gallis acciderunt* (1591, 14), states:

Jacques Le Moyne, also known as Morgues, ... a Frenchman and distinguished painter, as one of those fifteen who escaped with Laudonnière from the slaughter, witnessed and participated in the entire action. On his return he related the events in sequence to the King of France by whom he was urged to put them down on paper.... But he kept it private to himself and his friends and thus far was unwilling to publish it. But a few years afterwards, when the good Theodor de Bry ... was visiting London in England, he formed a great friendship with Morgues and at the same time gathered information on a great many questions to do with this story, so that the publication of these matters was agreed between them. Then, on Morgues's death, the aforesaid Theodor bought the narrative for himself from his widow.

Le Moyne, a Huguenot refugee and a protégé of Ralegh living in London, had in 1564 accompanied Laudonnière's expedition to Florida as its official artist and his narrative is illustrated with engravings after his drawings.[83] Hakluyt referred to Le Moyne's pictures in 1587 in the dedication to his English translation of Laudonnière (9): 'The chiefe things worthie observation in Florida are drawne in colours by James Morgues painter yet living in the Blacke Friers in London'.[84] Le Moyne's narrative, as printed by de Bry, draws at times on Laudonnière's own account, which, as we have seen, had been published at Hakluyt's instigation in 1586 (5). De Bry apparently first visited London in 1587, when he was commissioned to engrave *The Funeral Procession of Sir Philip Sidney*.[85] Although de Bry does not acknowledge Hakluyt's role in the publication of Le Moyne, it is likely that Hakluyt was the initial intermediary between Le Moyne and de Bry, as he had been with John White, the paths of Hakluyt, White and Le Moyne all crossing under their common patronage by Ralegh.

De Bry and his heirs went on to publish the greatest illustrated collection of voyages of the period, with instalments appearing until 1634. It would be an overstatement to say that Hakluyt inspired the entire project, but it is reasonable to suggest that he made de Bry aware of the possibilities.[86]

Hakluyt is very focused on the serious collection and presentation of texts, whereas de Bry's approach was much more entrepreneurial: the subsequent instalments of their voyages do not, I think, have the quality or originality of illustration of the first two parts and were much more determined by a calculation of the exotic and the sensational that might appeal to the book-buying public. Generally, and in contrast to Hakluyt's, the texts of the de Bry volumes leave much to be desired, but it was their abundant illustration that accounted for their great contemporary success.[87]

Intentions

What was Hakluyt's purpose? In the dedication to the *Divers Voyages* (1582) he drew attention to the 'great conquests' of the Spanish and Portuguese in America, the hope that the English might partake in this enterprise (one reason he gives is to release surplus population), and the opportunities to evangelise the heathen. He stresses English claims by right of prior discovery: the publication of evidence of this was therefore of implicit importance.[88] The book as a whole, as we have seen, was intended to gather information useful for those attempting similar trans-Atlantic ventures. His 1587 edition of Peter Martyr (8) is a clearer guide to his more ambitious project of collecting English voyages. The dedication to Sir Walter Ralegh[89] hails the good fortune of the Spanish in having Peter Martyr as the chronicler of their deeds in the New World and commends Ralegh for his efforts in America (apparently using the name Virginia for the first time in a printed book).[90] It makes two further significant points. First, a scholarly one, is that the scarce 1530 Alcalá edition[91] which Hakluyt was republishing, although the fullest, needed certain editorial improvements (including an index), which shows that Hakluyt saw himself as a responsible editor, not interested merely in issuing a simple reprint. Second, Hakluyt stressed the need 'to collect in orderly fashion the maritime records of our own countrymen, now lying scattered and neglected, and ... bring them to the light of day in a worthy guise, to the end that posterity ... may at last be inspired to seize the opportunity offered to them of playing a worthy part'. This is the first known reference by Hakluyt to his work on the *Principal Navigations of the English Nation*.

In his preface to the reader in the original (1589) edition of the *Principall Navigations* Hakluyt is quite clear about the organisation of his work and its grounding in reliable first-hand reports: 'I have referred every voyage to his author: for I am not ignorant of Ptolemies assertion, that *Peregrinationis historia* [the history of travel], and not those wearie volumes bearing the titles of universall cosmographie which some men that I could name have been published as their owne, beying in deed most untruly and unprofitablie ramassed and hurled together, is that which must bring us to the certayne and full discoverie of the world' (this is probably a dig at Thevet). He is also clear about the scope of his work: no 'action performed near home, nor in any part of Europe commonly frequented by our shipping' would be found in it, nor would voyages 'neither of search and discoverie of strange coasts, the chiefe subject of this my labour'.[92]

The *Principall Navigations* was not the first collection of voyages in English – that distinction must go to Richard Eden's *Decades of the Newe Worlde* (1555), which was much revised and expanded by Willes as the *History of Travayle* (1577).[93] Both of these include a few English voyages, Eden the English West African ('Guinea') voyages of the early 1550s, to which Willes added the Muscovy Company's ventures to Persia in the 1560s (Hakluyt drew on both these collections in compiling the *Principal Navigations*). But this content is minute compared to the whole, reflecting the relatively late English contribution to the discovery and description of distant lands in the sixteenth century. Hakluyt, however, concentrates on English enterprises, as he states in his preface: 'I meddle in this worke with the navigations onely of our own nation', allowing occasionally 'some strangers as witnesses', if their notices added to his central themes. This focus on English voyages – it should be noted that the coverage was not confined to the sixteenth century and Hakluyt includes not only medieval English travels, but also their British precedents in the accounts of the journeys of the Empress Helena and her son, Constantine the Great, as well as those of Arthur and the Welsh Madoc – makes the *Principal Navigations* unique in voyage collections of the period in being devoted to but one particular nation.[94] Ramusio's is a cosmopolitan collection, while the Spanish and the Portuguese, although writing much on the deeds of their countrymen, produced nothing comparable in terms of textual presentation or as a compendium of voyages.[95]

Between 1580, when Cartier's *Shorte and Briefe Narration* (1) was published, and his death in 1616, Hakluyt influenced or was directly responsible for the printing of no less than 26 travel books (excluding the manuscript *Discourse*; the total may be higher but 26 represents those in which his involvement is documented or unambiguous).[96] A rough total for the number of travel books, broadly defined, printed in England during this period is about 160.[97] Only four of Hakluyt's books, the *Divers Voyages*, the two editions of the *Principal Navigations*, and the edition of Harriot published by de Bry in Frankfurt, primarily concern English travels. The work of Hakluyt's successor, Samuel Purchas, whose massive collection of travels, *Purchas his Pilgrimes*, published in 1625 (**28**), was heavily indebted to Hakluyt, may be considered in part as an indication of what Hakluyt might have gone on to do in terms of coverage, not only updating, but also broadening it to include non-English accounts, reverting to the cosmopolitan coverage of Hakluyt's predecessors (and indeed successors).

The first publication of Purchas to reflect Hakluyt's involvement was the second edition of *Purchas his Pilgrimage. Or relations of the world and the religions observed in all ages and places discovered, from the Creation unto this present* (1614, **27**). Purchas met Hakluyt sometime after the publication of the first edition (1613) and in the second he acknowledged Hakluyt for making various new material available to him for inclusion in the second: 'Ramusius and M. Hakluit, in their books of voyages, have been two libraries unto me of many navigations and discoveries heere mentioned: and now in this edition I have beene much beholden to M. Hakluit for many written treatises in this kinde'.[98] Although the third edition (1617) was expanded, Purchas laments that Hakluyt, who had died in 1616, had not given him further assistance:

I could not obtaine like kindnes from him, I know not how affected or infected with emulation or jealousie; yet shall his name live whiles my writings endure, as without whose helpes and industrious collections, perhaps I had never troubled the worlde in this kinde. And this is my epitaph in his memorie; who hath yet a better, his owne large volumes being the best and truest titles of his honour: and if some *Juno Lucinca* would help to bring forth the posthume issue of his voyages not yet published, the world would enjoy a more full testimony of his paines in that kinde.[99]

The circumstances of their falling out remain uncertain, but eventually Hakluyt's papers passed to Purchas, whose *Pilgrimes* includes over 120 accounts derived from Hakluyt (at the end of his preface 'to the reader' in the first volume Purchas explains how he signifies the source of his texts, marking with an 'H' those 'borrowed from Master Hakluyts papers').[100] The letterpress title-page in each volume does not mention Hakluyt, but his influence is made explicit on the engraved general title, which reads *Hakluytus Posthumus or Purchas his Pilgrimes. Contayning a history of the world, in sea voyages & lande travells, by Englishmen & others ... Some left written by Mr Hakluyt at his death, more since added, his also perused & perfected.*

Impact and readership

Whether Hakluyt was being propagandist, as opposed to patriotic and anxious to add to the sum of geographical knowledge, in the *Principal Navigations* is debatable. Both editions, in folio, the second in three volumes, are too bulky to be effective vehicles for propaganda. His manuscript *Discourse of Western Planting*, articulating schemes associated with Ralegh for exploiting colonial opportunities in America, can certainly be deemed propagandist, although, as we have seen, it was not intended for widespread publication and was partly, at least, related to Hakluyt's quest for patronage. His edition of *Virginia Richly Valued* (21) is openly associated with the Virginia Company and is dedicated to its council. But it is notable that Hakluyt draws attention in the preface to the 1598 *Principal Navigations* to his inclusion of 'certaine fragments concerning the beginnings, antiquities, and grouth of the classical and warrelike shipping of this island: as namely, first of the great navie of that victorious Saxon prince, King Edgar ... '[101] and the book may be best seen in the context of the antiquarian and collecting movement of the circle of William Camden, as an episode in intellectual as much as colonial history. (Camden contributed a commendatory verse to the *Principal Navigations*. Like Hakluyt, he had Oxford and Westminster School connections, and had close links with Continental scholarship; as the *Principal Navigations* owed much to the Italian Ramusio, so Camden's *Britannia*, 1586, was inspired by chorographical methods pioneered in Italy by Flavio Biondo.)[102]

The book's readership and influence is more difficult to establish, although its contemporary ownership is well documented. Surviving copies include those of Robert Burton, Thomas Egerton, Lancelot Andrewes, John Selden, John Whitgift, Lord Lumley (whose library was used by Hakluyt), Sir Robert Cecil, Sir Ferdinando Gorges, Prince Henry, George Wilmer (a merchant and investor in the Virginia and East India Companies),[103] the 'Wizard Earl' of Northumberland[104] and Sir

Edward Coke[105]; in addition the book is well represented in various Oxford, Cambridge and cathedral libraries.[106] Gabriel Harvey recommended the work,[107] while Michael Drayton wrote of 'industrious Hackluit' in his ode 'To the Virginia Voyage'.[108] In France, the 1589 edition presented by Hakluyt to the poet, Philippe Desportes (d.1606) passed to the historian J. A. de Thou (d.1617).[109] A copy was obtained by the East India Company in 1611 'for the better comforte of such of our factors as are recideinge in the Indies ... to recreate their spirittes with varietie of historie' (other books included Foxe's *Book of Martyrs*)[110] and in the early 1620s a copy was bought from the Stationer, John Budge, for the use of the Virginia Company (price £1 16s).[111] Samuel Purchas published an account in his *Pilgrimes* (1625, **28**) of the third East India Company voyage (1607) which would have been forced to return to England had not a copy of Hakluyt been on board: after consulting it the crew was able to find a watering place on the coast of Sierra Leone. Purchas aptly commented in a side-note: 'M. Hackluits books of voyages are of great profit' and reported that Sir Thomas Smith, Governor of the East India Company, told him that this saved the Company £20,000, 'which they had bin endamaged if they had returned home, which necessitie had constrayned, if that Booke had not given light' (it is difficult, however, to generalise from this specific instance of the book's practical utility).[112]

The long-term impact of Hakluyt is to be found in the transmission of texts. To take but one example: Drake's circumnavigation, 'the famous voyage', the earliest proper account of the voyage to be published, was, as we have seen, first printed by Hakluyt in the 1589 *Principall Navigations*, again in 1598 (with a few small changes), by Purchas in 1625, and in the twentieth century it has been reprinted in Wagner's *Sir Francis Drake's Voyage around the World*.[113] Some printed texts survive only in their printing by Hakluyt: for example, in the 1589 *Principall Navigations* he printed the North American travels of David Ingram, which from Humphrey Dyson's seventeenth-century library catalogue were evidently printed in 1583 ('A true discourse of the adventures & travailes of David Ingram being sett on shore with 100 more of his fellowes by Captaine Hawkins in the heathen countries in 8° 1583'), but which no longer survives as a separate printing.[114] In the seventeenth century Hakluyt was used by Thévenot in compiling his *Relations de divers voyages curieux, qui n'ont point esté publiees; ou qui ont esté traduites d'Hacluyt, de Purchas, & d'autres voyageurs* (1663).[115] The great eighteenth-century voyage collections such as Harris's *Navigantium atque Itinerantium Bibliotheca:*

or, a compleat collection of voyages and travels: consisting of above four hundred of the most authentick writers; beginning with Hackluit, Purchass, &c. (1705),[116] drew on him, although the anonymous editors of *A Collection of Voyages and Travels* (1704) published by Awnsham and John Churchill to rival Harris were critical of Hakluyt, who it 'might be wished ... had been less voluminous, delivering what was really authentick and useful, and not stuffing his work with so many trading voyages that have nothing new in them, so many warlike exploits ... and other things little to the purpose of travels and discoveries'[117] (the preparation of the Churchills' collection is sometimes associated with John Locke, who owned a copy of the *Principal Navigations*).[118] The proposals issued in 1736 by the antiquary William Oldys 'for reprinting by subscription, the *Navigations &c. of the English Nation* by Ric. Hakluyt, M.A. &c., in one vol. folio' had to be abandoned because of insufficient support to warrant the expense involved. Nevertheless Oldys went on to publish in *The British Librarian* the first extensive bibliographical description of the *Principal Navigations*, while his pioneering and scholarly article on Hakluyt in *Biographia Britannica* is a serious bio-bibliographical essay that still repays reading today.[119] In 1809 the 1598–1600 *Principal Navigations* was reprinted in its entirety for the first time, with a supplement printing several works associated with Hakluyt in various ways.[120]

In varying contexts Hakluyt has been much consulted and discussed,[121] such as by Milton in his *Brief History of Moscovia* (1682),[122] whose marginal notes clearly indicate when he has used Hakluyt as a source, or by James Burney in his great *Chronological History of the Voyages and Discoveries in the South Sea or Pacific Ocean* (1803), where he remarked:

As an acknowledgement due to the labours of Mr Hakluyt, and the only return which can be made for the great assistance which has been derived from them in composing the present work, it is just to remark that his collection is more rich in original authorities concerning voyages and discoveries than any other work which has been published by a single individual.[123]

In the second half of the nineteenth century the Hakluyt Society, founded in 1846 and named in honour of Hakluyt as an editor of voyages and travels, included selections from his writings in volumes such as Collinson's *The Three Voyages of Martin Frobisher ... reprinted from the first edition of Hakluyt's Voyages, with selections from manuscript documents* (it should be stressed, however, that the great majority of texts printed by the Society to date are not from Hakluyt),[124] while the twentieth century has seen the scholarly quarrying of the *Principal Navigations* as part of such publications as Quinn's edition of the *Roanoke Voyages*,[125] frequent citation in the source-notes in monographs concerned with sixteenth-century voyaging and European expansion overseas,[126] as well as compendiums such as the Quinns' *Virginia Voyages from Hakluyt*[127] and Locke's *First Englishmen in India*,[128] which consists mainly of extracts from the *Principal Navigations*, and a paperback abridgement printing about one tenth of the 1598–1600 *Principal Navigations*.[129]

Hakluyt's very success in transmitting texts has been tentatively qualified by P. E. H. Hair, as he muses in his discussion of Hakluyt's probable diminishing usefulness in future scholarly study of the Guinea voyages:

The history of English mercantile venture in Guinea, as part of the history of English overseas enterprise, is of course an older study, and for a century Hakluyt has provided a basis and framework for research in this field. However, during this period scholars have also ransacked libraries and archives for manuscript sources, with considerable success, and it may be fairly said that the printed *Principal Navigations* continue to be used, apart from the convenience of consultation, only because the manuscripts on which the text was based are no longer extant. Non-survival is so regularly the case that it would seem that Hakluyt collected the only manuscript copy of any account, and that this copy was destroyed in the printing process. It follows that we must ask an ungracious question: would we now be better off for sources if Hakluyt had not made his collection? On the one hand, manuscripts collected by Hakluyt are not now extant (and whatever we think of Hakluyt's editing , we know that the texts he passed on to Purchas were mangled in printing), while manuscripts he did not collect are extant. Yet on the other hand, Hakluyt has preserved for us Baker's poems [recounting his voyages to Guinea], whose original print has not survived. Surely some of the manuscripts would have been similarly lost in the course of centuries; and may it not have been the good influence of the *Principal Navigations* which enabled some of the accounts which were not included to survive?[130]

Other qualifications made of Hakluyt's editing include his treatment of Marbeck's narrative of the Cadiz raid, the 'lively style' of which, Julian Corbett thought, 'seems to have displeased the Preacher, and in editing it for his collection of voyages he sadly mutilated it'.[131] An especially severe criticism has been levelled at his editing of Giles Fletcher's description of Russia in the first volume of the *Principal Navigations* (1598), which R. O. Lindsay has called 'puzzling, inconsistent, and misleading'.[132] It is important in evaluating Hakluyt as a documentary source to acknowledge such caveats, but, equally, one has to be careful not to impose anachronistic scholarly criteria that are best avoided if attempting to interpret Hakluyt within the context of his own time and audience.

In addition to the *Principal Navigations*, the 25 or so other printed books associated with him are further evidence of Hakluyt's influence in travel writing. It is probable that he was connected, if only loosely, with several other works, while at least one major project considered by him, an edition of the medieval Arabic geographer, Abulfida, did not reach fruition. John Newbery wrote to Hakluyt from Aleppo in May 1583 that on Hakluyt's behalf he was searching for the 'booke of Cosmographie of Abilfada Ismael, but by no meanes can heare of it. Some say that possibly it may be had in Persia, but notwithstanding I will not faile to make inquirie for it, both in Babylon, and in Balsara, and if I can finde it in any way of these places, I wil send it you from thence'.[133] As far as is known, Newbery was unsuccessful in this quest, but Hakluyt apparently obtained or knew of a copy elsewhere, for Ortelius wrote to William Camden in November 1588 that he had heard that Hakluyt was hopeful of producing an edition of Abulfida's geography,[134] and in December 1594 Hakluyt wrote to Emanuel van Meteren: 'Regarding Abilfeda Ismael, if that work is not to be had from the library in Heidelberg of my friend Mr Paulus Melissus, I can refer him to some of my friends at Venice who have copies translated into Latin'.[135] Although Abulfida had been referred to by Ramusio (which is how Hakluyt probably first became aware of his work), no edition appeared in Europe until 1650, edited by the English scholar, John Greaves.[136]

We see in these books that Hakluyt's achievement in terms of documenting the Western discovery of the distant corners of the globe was not confined to English voyages and that he brought to English readers a significant amount of material reflecting his Continental European experience and contacts – acquaintance with such figures as Gerard Mercator and Abraham Ortelius is attested for in his correspondence, while the Dutch consulted him in connection with Barents's voyages in the 1590s.[137] The first volume of the new *Oxford History of the British Empire* is generally dismissive of Hakluyt, with a few references to his work as 'propagandist' and militantly Protestant (but aspirational only, so deemed to be of little influence); even its special chapter on 'literature and empire' gives him but the briefest of mentions.[138] It is difficult to say exactly where this 'militant Protestantism' can be found in Hakluyt's texts, as opposed to conventional calls for evangelisation that might be expected from most people of the time, certainly an Anglican priest. There is no known link between Hakluyt and the publication of *The Spanish Colonie, or briefe chronicle of the acts … of the Spaniardes in the West Indies, called the Newe World* (1583),[139] an English translation of Bartolomé de las Casas's fervent denunciation of Spanish colonialism, which, from its first publication in Spanish in the 1550s, had been enthusiastically adopted throughout Protestant Europe as a potent anti-Spanish, and, by extension, anti-Catholic, tract. Hakluyt himself had no aversion to including the travels of the English Jesuit, Thomas Stevens (Stephens) to Goa in both editions of the *Principal Navigations*.[140] Perhaps, now that Hakluyt is relieved of his awkward imperial attachments, we can move on to examine his books, and those associated with him, in the context of geographical and historical learning and the spread of knowledge and the transmission of texts in Renaissance Europe. Hakluyt was English, but his work was not insular and reflects a rich Continental European context. Finally, it might be suggested that although Hakluyt himself drew attention to the utility of his texts in planning colonial projects, this could perhaps reflect the need for patrons whose association with such ventures might provide the source material for his books, and that the knowledge so gained was sufficient reason in itself for publication. In other words, Hakluyt's books were not incidental means to further an imperial objective, but ends in themselves, and deserve consideration in their own right as repositories of knowledge: empire might have served Richard Hakluyt's interests as much as he served empire's.

References

Abbreviations

Arber: Edward Arber, ed., *A Transcript of the Registers of the Company of Stationers of London, 1554–1640*, 5 vols (London: privately printed, 1875–94).

Census: P. A. Neville-Sington and Anthony Payne, 'An Interim Census of Surviving Copies of Hakluyt's *Divers Voyages* (1582) and *Principal Navigations* (1589; 1598/9–1600)', in Anthony Payne, *Richard Hakluyt and his Books* (London: Hakluyt Society, 1997), pp.25–76.

Church: George Watson Cole, *A Catalogue of Books relating to the Discovery and early History of North and South America, forming part of the library of E. D. Church*, 5 vols (New York: Dodd, Mead, 1907).

Neville-Sington: P. A. Neville-Sington, 'The Primary Purchas Bibliography', in L. E. Pennington, ed., *The Purchas Handbook*, 2 vols (London: Hakluyt Society, 1997), ii, pp.465–573.

Parks: George Bruner Parks, *Richard Hakluyt and the English Voyages*, second edition (New York: Frederick Ungar, 1961).

Quinn: D. B. and A. M. Quinn, 'A Hakluyt Chronology', 'Contents and Sources of the Three Major Works'; D. B. Quinn, C. E. Armstrong and R. A. Skelton, 'The Primary Hakluyt Bibliography', in D. B. Quinn, ed., *The Hakluyt Handbook*, 2 vols (London: Hakluyt Society, 1974), i, pp.263–331, ii, pp.335–460, 461–575.

STC: A. W. Pollard and G. R. Redgrave, *A Short-title Catalogue of Books printed in England, Scotland, & Ireland and of English Books printed abroad, 1475–1640*, second edition, revised by W. A. Jackson, F. S. Ferguson and K. F. Pantzer, 3 vols (London: Bibliographical Society, 1976–91).

Taylor: E. G. R. Taylor, ed., *The Original Writings & Correspondence of the Two Richard Hakluyts*, 2 vols (London: Hakluyt Society, 1935).

Wagner: Henry R. Wagner, *The Spanish Southwest, 1542–1794: an annotated bibliography*, second edition, 2 vols (Albuquerque: Quivira Society, 1937).

Notes

1.   Francisco López de Gómara, *La Istoria de las Indias* (1552), dedication to Charles V, and Adam Smith, *An Inquiry into the … Wealth of Nations* (1776), bk 4, ch. vii, quoted and discussed by J. H. Elliott, *The Old World and the New, 1492–1650* (Cambridge: Cambridge University Press, 1970), pp.1–10.

2.   1598–1600 *Principal Navigations*, i, dedication, Taylor, doc.73, p.426.

3.   Joseph Sabin, *A Dictionary of Books relating to America*, vol.vii (New York: J. Sabin and Sons, 1875), p.546.

4.   For example by John Carter and Percy H. Muir, *Printing and the Mind of Man: a descriptive catalogue illustrating the impact of print on the evolution of western civilization* (London: Cassell, 1967), p.63.

5.   J. A. Froude, 'England's Forgotten Worthies', *Westminster Review*, n.s., 2 (July and October 1852), pp.34–5.

6.   Quinn, p.265. For Hakluyt's immediate family, see Parks, pp.242–4 (and pp.235–6 for the spelling and pronunciation of the family name).

7.   1589 *Principall Navigations*, dedication, Taylor, doc.65, pp.396–7. For Richard Hakluyt the elder, see Parks, pp.25–55, 233–41.

8.   Lesley B. Cormack, *Charting an Empire: geography at the English universities, 1580–1620* (Chicago: University of Chicago Press, 1997), pp.58–66.

9.   1589 *Principall Navigations*, dedication, Taylor, doc.65, p.397.

10.   Quinn, pp.266–7.

11.   Taylor, doc.66, p.408, doc.76, p.458.

12.   G. D. Ramsay, 'Clothworkers, Merchants Adventurers and Richard Hakluyt', *English Historical Review*, 92 (1977), pp.504–21. For Hakluyt's sponsorship by the Clothworkers, see also Thomas Girtin, 'Mr Hakluyt, Scholar at Oxford', *Geographical Journal*, 69 (1953), pp.208–12 (I am grateful to Mr D. E. Wickham, Archivist to the Clothworkers' Company, for this reference) and Quinn, pp.268–9, 272, 280, 292–3. The Clothworkers' grant continued to be available until March 1587 but Hakluyt seems not to have claimed it after 1586, when he began to receive a stipend as a prebendary of Bristol Cathedral.

13.   Taylor, doc.66, p.403.

14.   G. D. Ramsay, 'Northern Europe', in D. B. Quinn, ed., *The Hakluyt Handbook*, 2 vols (London: Hakluyt Society, 1974), i, p.160.

15.   Quinn, p.286.

16. David Armitage, 'Literature and Empire', in Nicholas Canny, ed., *The Origins of Empire: British overseas enterprise to the close of the seventeenth century* (Oxford: Oxford University Press, 1998), pp.106–7.

17. Ciaran Brady, reviewing the 1993 Hakluyt Society facsimile edition, *Imago Mundi*, 49 (1997), p.168.

18. Taylor, doc.35, p.175; Parks, p.247.

19. Arber, ii, p.411.

20. Census, p.31.

21. D. B. Quinn, *Richard Hakluyt, Editor: a study introductory to the facsimile edition of Richard Hakluyt's Divers Voyages* (Amsterdam: Theatrum Orbis Terrarum, 1967), pp.27, 33.

22. 21 July 1584, in Albert Feuillerat, ed., *Sir Philip Sidney: The Defence of Poesie … Correspondence* (Cambridge: The University Press, 1923), p.145. Sidney's remark provides the title for P. A. Neville-Sington, 'A Very Good Trumpet: Richard Hakluyt and the politics of overseas expansion', in Cedric C. Brown and Arthur F. Marotti, eds, *Texts and Cultural Change in Early Modern England* (Basingstoke: Macmillan, 1997), pp.66–79.

23. Taylor, doc.40, p.199.

24. Stephen Parmenius, *De navigatione … carmen* (London: T. Purfoot, 1582, STC 19308; Church 127). See D. B. Quinn and Neil M. Cheshire, eds, *The New Found Land of Stephen Parmenius: the life and writings of a Hungarian poet, drowned on a voyage from Newfoundland, 1583* (Toronto: University of Toronto Press, 1972).

25. Arber, ii, p.529. The only references to Hakluyt in Conyers Read, *Mr Secretary Walsingham and the Policy of Queen Elizabeth*, 3 vols (Oxford: Clarendon Press, 1925) are to the *Principall Navigations* dedication and his despatch by Walsingham to Bristol in 1583 to raise mercantile support for Gilbert's North American ventures (iii, pp.404, 434–5).

26. Harry Kelsey, *Sir Francis Drake: the Queen's pirate* (New Haven: Yale University Press, 1998), pp.85–8, 177–9, 447–8. Walsingham's involvement in the inclusion of the Drake narrative (and, at the behest of the Muscovy Company, in the alteration of the account of Bowes's embassy to Russia) is conjectured by D. B. Quinn, 'Early Accounts of the Famous Voyage', in N. J. W. Thrower, ed., *Sir Francis Drake and the Famous Voyage, 1577–1580* (Berkeley: University of California Press, 1984), pp.33–48. The Census records the presence or not of the Drake leaves and the state of the Bowes account in surviving copies.

27. W. H. Kerr, 'The Treatment of Drake's Circumnavigation in Hakluyt's "Voyages", 1589', *Papers of the Bibliographical Society of America*, 34 (1940), p.295.

28. S. C. Lomas, ed., *Calendar of State Papers, Foreign Series … the Reign of Elizabeth*, vol.xix (London: HMSO, 1916), p.108.

29. Helen Wallis, 'The Cartography of Drake's Voyage', and Benjamin P. Draper, 'A Collection of Drake Bibliographic Items', in N. J. W. Thrower, ed., *Sir Francis Drake and the Famous Voyage* (Berkeley: University of California Press, 1984), pp.123–4, 191–2.

30. Taylor, doc.66, p.407.

31. Quinn, p.475.

32. Giles Fletcher, *Of the Russe Common Wealth* (London: T. D[awson] for Thomas Charde, 1591, STC 11056). For the Muscovy Company's complaint and evidence of

the book's suppression, see Lloyd E. Berry, ed., *The English Works of Giles Fletcher, the Elder* (Madison: University of Wisconsin Press, 1964), pp.150–4.

33. p.495.

34. See T. S. Willan, *The Early History of the Russia Company* (Manchester: Manchester University Press, 1956), pp.163–79.

35. Taylor, doc.66, pp.407–8. For Dyer, see Ralph M. Sargent, *At the Court of Elizabeth: the life and lyrics of Sir Edward Dyer* (Oxford: Oxford University Press, 1935). Sargent (p.73) fails to identify the Hakluyt sitting with Dyer on the 1581 Dover harbour commission as the elder Hakluyt (for this commission see Parks, pp.34, 239).

36. [John Dee], *General and Rare Memorials* (London: J. Day, 1577, STC 6459).

37. See William H. Sherman, *John Dee: the politics of reading and writing in the English Renaissance* (Amherst: University of Massachusetts Press, 1995), pp.152–81.

38. See J. O. Halliwell, ed., *The Private Diary of Dr John Dee* (London: Camden Society, 1842), pp.2, 4, 8, 18–19, 54, and Peter J. French, *John Dee* (London: Routledge and Kegan Paul, 1972), chs 6–8, *passim*.

39. Taylor, doc.76, pp.462–3.

40. For Cecil's patronage see Parks, pp.201–2; Quinn, pp.313–4, 316. For Hakluyt at Westminster Abbey see Quinn, pp.317–20, 322, 329–30.

41. Anthony Payne, *Richard Hakluyt and his Books* (London: Hakluyt Society, 1997), pp.13–15 (a discussion in the context of Elizabethan censorship). The Census records the presence or not of the Cadiz leaves in surviving copies.

42. The cancellation of the Cadiz leaves is often linked to Essex's political position: see [William Oldys], *The British Librarian* (London: T. Osborne, 1738), pp.158–9; Thomas Birch, *Memoirs of the Reign of Queen Elizabeth ... and ... her favourite, Robert Earl of Essex ... From the original papers of Antony Bacon*, 2 vols (London: A. Millar, 1754), ii, p.98; Julian S. Corbett, *The Successors of Drake* (London: Longmans, Green, 1900), p.440; Charles E. Armstrong, 'The Voyage to Cadiz in the Second Edition of Hakluyt's Voyages', *Papers of the Bibliographical Society of America*, 49 (1955), p.256; Quinn, p.491.

43. Mervyn James, 'At a Crossroads of the Political Culture: the Essex Revolt, 1601', in M. James, *Society, Politics and Culture* (Cambridge: Cambridge University Press, 1986), pp.461–2. P. E. J. Hammer, 'Myth-Making: politics, propaganda and the capture of Cadiz in 1596', *Historical Journal*, 40 (1997), pp.640–2.

44. Thomas Birch, *Memoirs of the Reign of Queen Elizabeth*, 2 vols (London: A. Millar, 1754), ii, p.95; R. B. Wernham, *The Return of the Armadas: the last years of the Elizabethan war against Spain* (Oxford: Clarendon Press, 1994), pp.122–3. P. E. J. Hammer, 'Myth-Making: ... the capture of Cadiz in 1596', *Historical Journal*, 40 (1997), p.632, states that the 1596 ban remained in force in 1598, forcing Hakluyt to remove the Cadiz material from the *Principal Navigations*.

45. For the politics of the Cadiz raid see P. E. J. Hammer, 'Patronage at Court, Faction and the Earl of Essex,' in John Guy, ed., *The Reign of Elizabeth I: court and culture in the last decade* (Cambridge: Cambridge University Press, 1995), pp.79–86.

46. Taylor, doc.73, pp.428–9.

47. Quinn, pp.382–3. Manuscript copies of Marbeck's account survive (and it may well have been circulated in this medium). The original of Hakluyt's narrative is BL Sloane MS 226.

48. Taylor, doc.74, p.450.

49. Roland White to Robert Sidney. C. L. Kingsford, ed., *Historical Manuscripts Commission: Report on the Manuscripts of Lord De L'Isle & Dudley*, vol. ii (London: HMSO, 1934), pp.390, 427.

50. P. S. Allen, 'Books brought from Spain in 1596', *English Historical Review*, 31 (1916), pp.606–10.

51. Quinn, pp.313–16, 324, 331.

52. Taylor, doc.89, p.499.

53. Quoted by Parks, p.221.

54. W. N. Sainsbury, ed., *Calendar of State Papers, Colonial Series, East Indies ... 1513–1616* (London: Longman, 1862), p.272.

55. Sir George Birdwood and William Foster, eds, *The Register of Letters &c. of the ... Company of Merchants of London trading into the East Indies, 1600–1619* (London: Bernard Quaritch, 1893), p.95, n.1.

56. Giovanni Battista Ramusio, *Primo Volume delle Navigationi et Viaggi; Secondo Volume; Terzo Volume* (Venice: Giunta, 1550, 1559, 1556). See George B. Parks, 'The Contents and Sources of Ramusio's *Navigationi*', *Bulletin of the New York Public Library*, 59 (1955), pp.279–313.

57. George B. Parks, 'Ramusio's Literary History', *Studies in Philology*, 52 (1955), p.127.

58. Sig. *5r.

59. Frances Yates, *John Florio* (Cambridge: The University Press, 1934), pp.53–60.

60. Taylor, doc.29, p.164–5.

61. Taylor, doc.35, pp.180–1.

62. Census, p.28.

63. Richard Willes, *The History of Travayle* (London: R. Jugge, 1577, STC 649; Church 119). For Willes's life see A. D. S. Fowler, ed., *De re poetica by Richard Will[e]s* (Oxford: Luttrell Society, 1958), pp.2–21.

64. Parks, pp.99–122; Quinn, pp.278–300.

65. Letter to Walsingham, 7 January 1584, Taylor, doc.44, p.206.

66. See Robert W. Karrow, *Mapmakers of the Sixteenth Century* (Chicago: Speculum Orbis Press, 1993), pp.529–46.

67. Taylor, doc.76, p.457.

68. Quinn, p.292, quoting Thevet's complaint from his manuscript *La grand insulaire*.

69. Quinn, pp.294–5; Colin Steele, *English Interpreters of the Iberian New World ... a bibliographical study, 1603–1726* (Oxford: Dolphin Book Co., 1975), pp.43–4.

70. For Espejo see Wagner, i, pp.153–63.

71. Dee also gave a copy of Hakluyt's 1587 edition of Peter Martyr to Harriot. Julian Roberts and Andrew G. Watson, eds, *John Dee's Library Catalogue* (London: Bibliographical Society, 1990), D1, D8.

72. *New Mexico. Otherwise, the voiage of Anthony de Espejo* (London: [T. East?] for Thomas Cadman, [1587], STC 18487; Wagner 8b); Parks, pp.249–50.

73. The titles of the re-issues give Hakluyt greater prominence, *The Historie of the West-Indies ... Published in Latin by Mr Hakluyt* (London: for Andrew Hebb, [c.1625]) and *The Famous Historie of the Indies ... Set forth first by Mr Hackluyt* (London: for Michael Sparke, 1628) (STC 651–2).

74. Juan González de Mendoza, *Historia ... del gran reyno dela China* (Madrid: Q. Gerardo for B. de Robles, 1586, Wagner 7y; original version, Rome: V. Accolti for B. Grassi, 1585, Wagner 7). Both went through numerous editions and translations: see Wagner, i, pp.116–53.

75. W. E. Retana, *Aparato bibliográfico de la historia general de Filipinas*, 3 vols (Madrid: M. Minuesa de los Ríos, 1906), i, pp.13–27.

76. Sir George Staunton and R. H. Major, eds, *The History of … China … reprinted from the early translation of R. Parke*, 2 vols (London: Hakluyt Society, 1853–4). From Major's introduction, i, pp.lxxxi–lxxxii, it is clear that he was unaware of the additional matter in the Madrid edition; for editorial confusion see ii, p.207, n.1.

77. STC, iii, pp.185–6; Denis B. Woodfield, *Surreptitious Printing in England, 1550–1640* (New York: Bibliographical Society of America, 1973), pp.5–18, 24–33. Wolfe also published an Italian translation of the González de Mendoza text without the Espejo relation (i.e. derived from the 1585 Rome original), with the false imprint 'In Vinegia. 1587. Per Andrea Muschio' (STC 12004; Wagner 7n; Woodfield 28).

78. Taylor, doc.66, p.409.

79. Arthur M. Hind, *Engraving in England in the Sixteenth and Seventeenth Centuries*, part i, *The Tudor Period* (Cambridge: The University Press, 1952), p.179.

80. R. A. Skelton, 'Hakluyt's Maps', in D. B. Quinn, ed., *The Hakluyt Handbook*, 2 vols (London: Hakluyt Society, 1974), i, pp.48–73.

81. First published as *A Briefe and True Report of … Virginia* (London: [R. Robinson], 1588, STC 12785; Church 135). See also John W. Shirley, *Thomas Harriot* (Oxford: Clarendon Press, 1983), pp.144–50.

82. Paul Hulton and D. B. Quinn, *The American Drawings of John White*, 2 vols (London: British Museum, 1964), i, pp.65-151 *passim*, ii, plates 119-43.

83. Paul Hulton, *The Work of Jacques Le Moyne de Morgues, a Huguenot artist in France, Florida and England*, 2 vols (London: British Museum, 1977), i, pp.87–113, 117–52 (modern English translation), 201–16, ii, plates 91–134. The exact dates of de Bry's visits to London are uncertain, but Hulton's discussion suggests they were in 1587 and after Le Moyne's death in 1588 (i, pp.11, 49, n.23). John Alden and Dennis C. Landis, eds, *European Americana: a chronological guide to works printed in Europe relating to the Americas*, vol.i (New York: Readex Books, 1980), 591/38, ascribes de Bry's *America*, part ii, to Laudonnière as an edition of his account first published in 1586.

84. Taylor, doc.58, p.373.

85. Engraved after Thomas Lant. Arthur M. Hind, *Engraving in England*, part i, *The Tudor Period* (Cambridge: The University Press, 1952), pp.132-7. Dyer and Drake are two associates of Hakluyt portrayed in the procession.

86. The most informative bibliographical treatment of de Bry is Church, i, pp.316–478, ii, pp.479–580. Parks (pp.161-3) puts a stronger emphasis on Hakluyt's influence on de Bry.

87. Donald F. Lach and Edwin J. Van Kley, *Asia in the Making of Europe*, vol.iii, bk 1 (Chicago: University of Chicago Press, 1993), p.516.

88. Taylor, doc.35, pp.175–81. For the claim of prior discovery in imperial thought, see Anthony Pagden, *Lords of all the World: ideologies of empire in Spain, Britain and France* (New Haven: Yale University Press, 1995), pp.80–3.

89. Taylor, doc.56, pp.356–69.

90. S. A. Dickson, *Tobacco: a catalogue of books … in the Arents Tobacco Collection*, part i (New York: New York Public Library, 1958), p.11.

91. Church 62.

92. Taylor, doc.66, pp.402–3. For a modern assessment of Thevet and the demise of his cosmography, see Frank Lestringant, *Mapping the Renaissance World: the geographical imagination in the age of discovery* (Cambridge: Polity Press, 1994), pp.126–31.

93. Richard Eden, *The Decades of the Newe Worlde or West India* (London: W. Powell, 1555, STC 645–8; Church 102). For Willes see note 63.

94. Taylor, doc.66, p.402. For Hakluyt's inclusion of medieval accounts in the context of Welsh antiquarian thought and Tudor dynastic ambitions, see Peter Roberts, 'Tudor Wales, National Identity and the British Inheritance', in Brendan Bradshaw and P. Roberts, eds, *British Consciousness and Identity: the making of Britain, 1533–1707* (Cambridge: Cambridge University Press, 1998), pp.29–33. For Hakluyt's interest in King Arthur see Jennifer R. Goodman, *Chivalry and Exploration, 1298–1630* (Woodbridge: Boydell Press, 1998), pp.172–4.

95. For general surveys of sixteenth-century travel literature, see Donald F. Lach, *Asia in the Making of Europe*, vol.i, bk 1, pp.148–217, vol.ii, bk 2, *passim* (Chicago: University of Chicago Press, 1965, 1977); and Boies Penrose, *Travel and Discovery in the Renaissance* (Cambridge, MA: Harvard University Press, 1952), ch.17. For a comparative discussion of the epic *Lusiads* of Camões and the *Principal Navigations*, see Richard Helgerson, *Forms of Nationhood: the Elizabethan writing of England* (Chicago: University of Chicago Press, 1992), pp.155–81.

96. See Quinn, pp.571–5, for works the publication of which Hakluyt may have influenced.

97. A rough estimate calculated from the entries on pp.249–63 of the chronological bibliographical list in John Parker, *Books to Build an Empire: a bibliographical history of English overseas interests to 1620* (Amsterdam: N. Israel, 1965). Parker's list includes new editions and is broadly defined to include navigational and other related works.

98. Sig. A5, quoted by Quinn, p.329.

99. p.972.

100. C. R. Steele, 'From Hakluyt to Purchas', in D. B. Quinn, ed., *The Hakluyt Handbook*, 2 vols (London: Hakluyt Society, 1974), i, pp.74–96; see also L. E. Pennington, ed., *The Purchas Handbook*, 2 vols (London: Hakluyt Society, 1997), Index, under 'Purchas, use of Hakluyt's papers and published accounts'.

101. Taylor, doc.74, p.447.

102. Anthony Payne, *Richard Hakluyt and his Books* (London: Hakluyt Society, 1997), p.10. F. J. Levy, 'The Making of Camden's *Britannia*', *Bibliothèque d'humanisme et renaissance*, 26 (1964), pp.70–97.

103. Census, pp.34, 38, 48–9, 50, 52, 57, 67. Hakluyt acknowledged use of Lumley's 'excellent librarie' in the *Principal Navigations*, Taylor, doc.74, p.437.

104. At Alnwick Castle: overlooked by the Census but recorded by G. R. Batho, 'The Library of the "Wizard" Earl: Henry Percy, Ninth Earl of Northumberland (1564–1632)', *The Library*, third series, 15 (1960), p.260, as vol.i (only) of the *Principal Navigations*. The third Harvard copy (Census, p.71) has the stamp of the Ninth and Tenth Earls, as illustrated by Batho, plate i(b). I am grateful to Professor Batho and Mr Roger Stoddard, Curator of Rare Books, Houghton Library, Harvard, for their help in identifying these copies.

105. Not in the Census. Vol.iii of Coke's *Principal Navigations*, its title inscribed 'Edw. Coke', survives in an English private collection. I am grateful to Dr Bent Juel-Jensen for this information. Coke's Hakluyt is not in W. O. Hassall, ed., *A Catalogue of the Library of Sir Edward Coke* (New Haven: Yale University Press, 1950), which, among other travel books, records his Purchas, Laudonnière and Ramusio (entries 553, 617, 982).

106. Census, pp.35, 62, 63.

107. Quinn, p.306 (quoting Harvey's commendation of the *Principall Navigations* as 'a worke of importance' in *Pierces Supererogation*, 1593).

108. Quinn, p.322. 'To the Virginia Voyage' was first printed in Drayton's *Poemes Lyrick and Pastorall*, 1606.

109. Census, p.41.

110. Sir George Birdwood and William Foster, eds, *The Register of Letters &c. of the ... Company of Merchants of London trading into the East Indies, 1600-1619* (London: Bernard Quaritch, 1893), p.419.

111. D. B. Quinn, 'A List of Books purchased for the Virginia Company', in Quinn, *Explorers and Colonies* (London: Hambledon Press, 1990), p.385.

112. *Purchas his Pilgrimes*, i, bk 3, ch.vi, p.188. Hakluyt's 'works' were recorded in the library at the East India Company's Fort St George in 1729: see Howard T. Fry, *Alexander Dalrymple* (London: Frank Cass, 1970), p.102.

113. Wagner, i, pp.163-7 (noting French derivatives as well). Henry R. Wagner, *Sir Francis Drake's Voyage around the World* (San Francisco: John Howell, 1926), pp.238-85 (including a discussion of the sources).

114. Cited by W. A. Jackson, 'Humphrey Dyson's Library, or, some observations on the survival of books', *Papers of the Bibliographical Society of America*, 43 (1949), p.285.

115. Melchisedech Thévenot, *Relations de divers voyages curieux ... premiere partie* (Paris: Jacques Langlois, 1663).

116. John Harris, *Navigantium atque Itinerantium Bibliotheca: or, a compleat collection of voyages and travels*, 2 vols (London: T. Bennet, 1705).

117. *A Collection of Voyages and Travels*, 4 vols (London: A. and J. Churchill, 1704). See in general G. R. Crone and R. A. Skelton, 'English Collections of Voyages and Travels, 1625-1846', in Edward Lynam, ed., *Richard Hakluyt & his Successors* (London: Hakluyt Society, 1946), pp.78-133 (quotation from p.79).

118. Census, p.67, sold at Christie's in 1993 (present location unknown). See also John Harrison and Peter Laslett, *The Library of John Locke*, second edition (Oxford: Clarendon Press, 1971), 1374, and pp.19, 28.

119. [William Oldys], *The British Librarian* (London: T. Osborne, 1738), pp.136-58. *Biographia Britannica*, vol.iv (London: W. Meadows, 1757). Oldys's article is unsigned. The 1736 proposals are noted on p.2472.

120. *Hakluyt's Collection of the Early Voyages, Travels, and Discoveries of the English Nation. A new edition, with additions*, 5 vols (London: R. H. Evans, 1809-12). Vol.iv, p.393 to end and vol.v comprise a Supplement, also issued separately as *A Selection of Curious, Rare and Early Voyages and Histories of Interesting Discoveries, chiefly published by Hakluyt, or at his suggestion, but not included in his celebrated compilation, to which, to Purchas and other general collections, this is intended as a supplement* (London: R. H. Evans, 1812). These are: *a.* 'Galvano's Discoveries of the World'; *b.* 'The Worldes Hydrographical Description, by J. Davis'; *c.* 'Voyage d'Outremer et retour de Jérusalem par la voie de terre, pendant le cours des années 1432 et 1433, par Bertrandon de la Brocquière'; *d.* 'The Navigation ... of Lewes Vertomanus'; *e.* 'A Voyage made by Certaine Ships of Holland into the East Indies ... 1597'; *f.* 'The Prosperous and Speedy Voyage to Java in the East Indies, performed by a fleete of 8 ships of Amsterdam ... 1598'; *g.* 'New from the East Indies: or a voyage to Bengalla'; *h.* 'The Fardle of Facions, conteining the aunciente maners, customes and lawes of ... Affricke and Asie'; *i.* 'The Conqueste of the Grand Canaries'; *j.* 'The Historie of the West Indies ... published in Latin by Hakluyt and translated by Lok'; *k.* 'Virginia

Richly Valued'; *l*. 'A Discovery of the Bermudas ... by Sir Thomas Gates ... set forth by Sil. Jourdan'; *m*. 'A True Coppie of a Discourse written by a Genteleman, employed in the late voyage of Spaine and Portingale ... 1589'; *n*. 'Omissions of Cales Voyage, stated and discussed by the Earl of Essex, from a manuscript in the possession of the Marquis of Stafford'.

121. See D. B. Quinn, 'Hakluyt's Reputation', and L. E. Pennington, 'Secondary Works on Hakluyt and his Circle', in D. B. Quinn, ed., *The Hakluyt Handbook*, 2 vols (London: Hakluyt Society, 1974), i, pp.133-52, ii, pp.576-610.

122. John Milton, *A Brief History of Moscovia* (London: M. Flesher for B. Aylmer, 1682). Annotated edition by G. B. Parks in *Complete Prose Works of John Milton*, vol.viii (New Haven: Yale University Press, 1982), pp.454-538.

123. James Burney, *A Chronological History of the ... Pacific Ocean*, 5 vols (London: Luke Hansard for G. and W. Nicol, 1803-17), ii, p.107.

124. Richard Collinson, ed., *The Three Voyages of Martin Frobisher* (London: Hakluyt Society, 1867). For the Hakluyt Society and a listing of its publications, see R. C. Bridges and P. E. H. Hair, eds, *Compassing the Vaste Globe of the Earth: studies in the history of the Hakluyt Society* (London: Hakluyt Society, 1996).

125. D. B. Quinn, ed., *The Roanoke Voyages, 1584-1590: documents to illustrate the English voyages to North America under the patent granted to Walter Raleigh*, 2 vols (London: Hakluyt Society, 1955).

126. For example Kenneth R. Andrews, *Trade, Plunder and Settlement: maritime enterprise and the genesis of the British empire, 1480-1630* (Cambridge: Cambridge University Press, 1984).

127. D. B. and A. M. Quinn, eds, *Virginia Voyages from Hakluyt* (London: Oxford University Press, 1973).

128. J. Courtenay Locke, ed., *The First Englishmen in India: letters and narratives of sundry Elizabethans written by themselves and edited with an introduction and notes* (London: George Routledge and Sons, 1930).

129. Jack Beeching, ed., *Hakluyt: Voyages and Discoveries* (Harmondsworth: Penguin Books, 1972).

130. P. E. H. Hair, 'Guinea', in D. B. Quinn, ed., *The Hakluyt Handbook*, 2 vols (London: Hakluyt Society, 1974), i, p.207. Baker's verse accounts of his voyages to Guinea were printed by Hakluyt in the 1589 *Principall Navigations*, possibly from *The Brefe Dyscource of Roberte Baker in Gynney*, a work licensed to Francis Coldoke in 1567/8 but not extant (Arber, i, p.363).

131. Julian S. Corbett, *The Successors of Drake* (London: Longmans, Green, 1900), p.442.

132. Robert O. Lindsay, 'Richard Hakluyt and Of the Russe Commonwealth', *Papers of the Bibliographical Society of America*, 57 (1963), p.326.

133. Taylor, doc.39, p.198.

134. Quinn, p.300.

135. Taylor, doc.71, p.420.

136. Giorgio Levi della Vida, *Ricerche sulla formazione del più antico fondo dei manoscritti orientali della Biblioteca Vaticana* (Vatican City: Biblioteca Apostolica Vaticana, 1939), pp.326, 334-5.

137. For Mercator see Taylor, doc.26, p.159; Ortelius, Quinn, p.268; Barents, Parks, pp.142-7, Quinn, pp.307-8.

138. Nicholas Canny, ed., *The Origins of Empire* (Oxford: Oxford University Press, 1998), pp.4-5, 106-7.

139. Bartolomé de las Casas, *The Spanish Colonie* (London: [T. Dawson] for W. Brome, 1583, STC 4739; Church 130). Quinn notes (p.572) that Hakluyt did, however, use this text in compiling his *Discourse of Western Planting*.

140. Stevens's account, in a letter written to his father from Goa in 1579, was mistakenly taken by John Newbery when he conferred with Hakluyt about eastern travels, for which he apologised and returned it in a letter to Hakluyt from Aleppo in 1583 (Taylor, doc.39, p.198). Despite religious differences Stevens had a reputation for protecting Englishmen at Goa: see Georg Schurhammer, 'Thomas Stephens, 1549–1619', *The Month*, n.s., 13 (April 1955), p.205.

Checklist of books by, or associated with, Richard Hakluyt

1. [Cartier, Jacques.] *A Shorte and Briefe Narration of the two Navigations and Discoveries to the Northweast Partes called Newe France: first translated out of French into Italian, by … Gio. Bapt. Ramutius, and now turned into English by John Florio: worthy the reading of all venturers, travellers, and discoverers.* London: Henry Bynneman, 1580 (Quinn, pp.272, 528; STC 4699; Church 125). Translated at Hakluyt's instigation and expense.

2. [Hakluyt, Richard.] *Divers Voyages touching the Discoverie of America, and the Ilands adjacent unto the same, made first of all by our Englishmen, and afterward by the Frenchmen and Britons: and certaine notes of advertisements for observations, necessarie for such as shall heereafter make the like attempt.* London: [Thomas Dawson] for Thomas Woodcock, 1582 (Quinn, pp.274, 338–40, 461–2; STC 12624; Census, pp.28–31; Church 128).

3. Hakluyt, Richard. 'A Particuler Discourse concerninge the greate necessitie and manifolde commodyties that are like to growe to this Realme of Englande by the Westerne Discoveries lately attempted, written … at the … direction of … Walter Raghly'. 1584 (Quinn, pp.284–6; Taylor, doc.46, pp.211–326; facsimile edition, ed. D. B. and A. M. Quinn, London: Hakluyt Society, 1993). Circulated in manuscript only.

4. Pigafetta, Marco Antonio. *Itinerario.* London: John Wolfe, 1585 (Quinn, pp.286, 530; STC 19914; Parks, p.249). Publication exhorted by Hakluyt.

5. Laudonnière, René Goulaine de. *L'histoire notable de la Floride … contenant les trois voyages faits en icelle par certains capitaines & pilotes françois, descrits par le Capitainne Laudonniere, qui y a commandé l'espace d'un an trois moys: à laquelle a esté adjousté un quatriesme voyage fait par le Capitaine Gourgues. Mise en lumiere par M[artin] Basanier.* Paris: Guillaume Auvray, 1586 (Quinn, pp.288–9, 292, 532; Church 131). Printed at Hakluyt's expense.

6. Espejo, Antonio de. *El viaje que hizo Antonio de Espejo en el anno de ochenta y tres: el qual con sus companneros descubrieron una tierra … a quien pusieron por nombre nuevo Mexico.* Paris: at the expense of Richard Hakluyt, 1586 (Quinn, p.468; Wagner 8).

7. Espejo, Antonio de. *Histoire des terres nouvellement descouvertes … nommees le nouveau Mexico … Traduict de l'espagnol en langue françoise, par M[artin] Basanier.* Paris: widow of Nicolas Roffet, 1586 (Quinn, pp.290, 534; Wagner 8a). Dedicated to Anne, duc de Joyeuse, not to Hakluyt as stated by Quinn. Hakluyt had reprinted the original Spanish text in Paris earlier in 1586 (6).

8. Anghiera, Pietro Martire d' (Peter Martyr). *De Orbe Novo Petri Martyris Anglerii Mediolanensis … decades octo, diligenti temporum observatione, & utilissimis annotationibus illustratae, suóque nitori restitutae, labore & industria Richardi Hakluyti Oxoniensis Angli. Additus est in usum lectoris accuratus totius operis index.* Paris: Guillaume Auvray, 1587 (Quinn, pp.293, 472; Church 133). Edited by Hakluyt.

9. Laudonnière, René Goulaine de. *A Notable Historie containing Foure Voyages made by certayne French Captaynes unto Florida: wherein the great riches and fruitefulnes of the countrey ... are brought to light, written all, saving the last, by Mousieur Laudonniere, who remained there himselfe as the French king's lieutenant a yere and a quarter: newly translated out of French into English by R. H[akluyt].* London: Thomas Dawson, 1587 (Quinn, pp.293-4, 470; STC 15316; Church 132).

10. González de Mendoza, Juan. *The Historie of the Great and Mightie Kingdome of China ... of Spanish by R[obert] Parke.* London: John Wolfe for Edward White, 1588 (Quinn, pp.302, 536; STC 12003; Church 134; Wagner 7jj). Translated at the request and encouragement of Hakluyt.

11. Hakluyt, Richard. *The Principall Navigations, Voiages and Discoveries of the English Nation, made by sea or over land, to the most remote and farthest distant quarters of the earth at any time with the compasse of these 1500 yeeres.* London: George Bishop and Ralph Newberie, deputies to Christopher Barker, 1589 (Quinn, pp.303, 341-77, 474-8; STC 12625; Census, pp.32-46; Church 139).

12. Meierus, Albertus. *Certaine Briefe, and Speciall Instructions for Gentlemen, Merchants, Students, Souldiers, Marriners, &c. employed in services abrode.* London: John Wolfe, 1589 (Quinn, pp.302, 538; STC 17784; Parks, p.120). Translated by Philip Jones and dedicated to Sir Francis Drake, probably at Hakluyt's suggestion.

13. Harriot, Thomas. Bry, Theodor de, *publisher. [America, part i] A Briefe and True Report of the New Found Land of Virginia.* Frankfurt: Johann Wechel for Theodor de Bry, 1590 (Quinn, pp.304, 540; STC 12786; Church 204). Publication facilitated by Hakluyt. Commentaries on the engravings after John White translated by Hakluyt. Also published in French, German and Latin.

14. Le Moyne de Morgues, Jacques. Bry, Theodor de, *publisher. [America, part ii] Brevis narratio eorum quae in Florida Americae provincia Gallis acciderunt, secunda in illam navigatione, duce Renato de Laudonniere classis praefecto: anno MDLXIIII.* Frankfurt: Johann Wechel for Theodor de Bry, 1591 (Quinn, pp.304, 542; Church 145). Le Moyne's narrative draws on Laudonnière's account published at Hakluyt's instigation (5). Hakluyt was probably the intermediary between de Bry and Le Moyne. Also published in German.

15. Lopes, Duarte. *A Report of the Kingdome of Congo ... Drawen out of the writings ... of Odoardo Lopez, a Portingall, by Philippo Pigafetta. Translated out of Italian by Abraham Hartwell.* London: [John Windet for] John Wolfe, 1597 (Quinn, pp.310, 544; STC 16805). Translated at the urging of Hakluyt. Dedicated to John Whitgift, Archbishop of Canterbury, not to George Abbot as stated by Quinn.

16. Hakluyt, Richard. *The Principal Navigations, Voiages, Traffiques and Discoveries of the English Nation, made by sea or over-land, to the remote and farthest distant quarters of the Earth, at any time within the compasse of these 1500 yeeres: devided into three severall volumes, according to the positions of the regions, whereunto they were directed.* London: George Bishop, Ralph Newbery and Robert Barker, 1598-99-1600 (Quinn, pp.311-14, 378-460, 490-511; STC 12626; Census, pp.47-61). 3 volumes. The title of vol.i in some copies is a cancel dated 1599 (Quinn, p.500; STC 12626a; Census, pp.62-76; Church 322).

17. Linschoten, Jan Huygen van. *John Huighen van Linschoten. His Discours of Voyages unto y' Easte & West Indies.* London: [John Windet for] John Wolfe, (1598) (Quinn, pp.310-11, 546; STC 15691; Church 321). Translated by William Phillip. Publication recommended by Hakluyt, who supplied the Dutch original for translation.

18. Leo Africanus, Johannes. *A Geographical Historie of Africa, written in Arabicke and Italian by John Leo a More ... Translated and collected by John Pory.* London: [Eliot's Court Press,] at the expense of George Bishop, 1600 (Quinn, pp.314, 548; STC 15481). Translated at Hakluyt's persuasion and published with an approbation by him.

19. Galvão, Antonio. *The Discoveries of the World from their first originall unto ... 1555. Briefly written in the Portugall tongue by Antonie Galvano, Governour of Ternate, ... and now published in English by Richard Hakluyt.* London: [Eliot's Court Press,] at the expense of George Bishop, 1601 (Quinn, pp.316, 522; STC 11543; Church 323).

20. Neck, Jacob Corneliszoon van. *The Journall ... of the Voyage ... of Jacob Corneliszen Neck, ... which sayled from Amsterdam the first day of March, 1598.* London: [Simon Stafford and Felix Kingston] for Cuthbert Burby and John Flasket, 1601 (Quinn, pp.317, 550; STC 18417). Translated by William Walker with Hakluyt's encouragement.

21. A Gentleman of Elvas. *Virginia Richly Valued, by the description of the maine land of Florida, her next neighbour: out of the foure yeeres continuall travell and discoverie ... of Don Ferdinando de Soto ... Written by a Portugall gentleman of Elvas, emploied in all the action, and translated out of Portugese by Richard Hakluyt.* London: Felix Kingston for Matthew Lownes, 1609 (Quinn, pp.323, 524; STC 22938; Church 337).

22. [Lescarbot, Marc.] *Nova Francia: or the description of that part of New France, which is one continent with Virginia. Described in the three late voyages and plantation made by Monsieur de Monts, Monsieur du Pont-Gravé, and Monsieur de Poutrincourt ... Translated out of French into English by P[ierre] E[rondelle].* London: [Eliot's Court Press,] at the expense of George Bishop, 1609 (Quinn, pp.324, 554; STC 15491; Church 341). Translated at Hakluyt's direction.

23. [Veer, Gerit de.] *The True and Perfect Description of Three Voyages, so strange and woonderful, one after the other, by the ships of Holland and Zeland, on the north sides of Norway, Muscovia, and Tartaria ... where never any man had bin before.* London: [William White] for Thomas Pavier, 1609 (Quinn, pp.323-4, 552; STC 24628). Translated by William Phillip with the encouragement of Hakluyt.

24. Anghiera, Pietro Martire d' (Peter Martyr). *De Novo Orbe, or the Historie of the West Indies, contayning the actes and adventures of the Spanyardes, which have conquered and peopled those countries ... Comprised in eight decades. Written by Peter Martyr a Millanoise of Angleria, Cheife Secretary to the Emperour Charles the fift ... Whereof three, have beene formerly translated into English, by R. Eden, whereunto the other five, are newly added by ... M[ichael] Lok.* London: [Thomas Dawson] for Thomas Adams, 1612 (Quinn, pp.327, 558; STC 650; Church 358). Translated with the encouragement of Hakluyt, whose 1587 Latin edition (8) was used for translating those decades not already translated by Eden in *The Decades of the Newe Worlde* (1555, STC 645).

25. Arthus, Gothard. *Dialogues in the English and Malaiane Languages: or, certaine common formes of speech, first written in Latin, Malaian, and Madagascar tongues ... and now faithfully translated into English tongue by Augustine Spalding, merchant, for their sakes, who happily shall hereafter undertake a voyage to the East-Indies.* London: Felix Kingston for William Welby, 1614 (Quinn, pp.328, 568; STC 810). The initial translation was done by Hakluyt.

26. Pitiscus, Bartholomew. *Trigonometry; or the doctrine of triangles. First written in Latine ... and now translated into English, by Ra. Handson.* (London: Edward Allde) for John Tapp, (1614) (Quinn, pp.329, 566; STC 19967). Translated and published at the persuasion of Hakluyt.

27. Purchas, Samuel. *Purchas his Pilgrimage. Or relations of the world and the religions observed in all ages and places discovered, from the Creation unto this present. The second edition ... much enlarged.* London: William Stansby for Henry Fetherstone, 1614 (Quinn, pp.329, 564; STC 20506; Neville-Sington, pp.482-4). Includes new material supplied by Hakluyt.

28. Purchas, Samuel. *Purchas his Pilgrimes.* London: William Stansby for Henry Fetherstone, 1625 (STC 20509; Church 401A; Neville-Sington, pp.519-50). 4 volumes. The engraved general title begins *Hakluytus Posthumus or Purchas his Pilgrimes.* Includes much material derived from Hakluyt.

Shipwrecks in print;
representations of maritime disaster in the late seventeenth century

MICHAEL HARRIS

MOST PEOPLE WHO WERE active travellers during the late seventeenth and early eighteenth centuries were likely to experience one or more of a range of disasters. Shipwreck and associated accidents only represented a part of the risk. Even so, water was a particularly dangerous element and as sailors were the greatest travellers so shipwreck figured largely in the catalogue of personal jeopardies.[1] This paper is about representations of this particular form of closure. Journeys which began but did not end, at least not in the way or not in the place originally intended. Paradoxically, shipwreck could also form a beginning. Narratives of individual suffering and adventure led back to starting points and to publication. These alternative journeys made by survivors, real or imagined, lurked within the huge literature of travel aimed at all sectors of the market. Ships and the movement of shipping had a particular cultural, commercial and even psychological force within English society and in trying to pin down some of the ways in which this material was constructed and marketed through the medium of print, all sorts of variables begin to emerge

This paper is in two overlapping parts. First, there will be an attempt to indicate the way in which information about shipwrecks was deployed within the print culture of the late seventeenth century, specifically through the newspaper coverage of all areas of maritime activity. Secondly, there will be an attempt to indicate how this core of information was extended into separate publications concerned with shipwrecks which came on to the market in a variety of guises.

First, then, how did ships and shipwrecks figure in print through the news serials published in London under the Licensing System (as well as during the periods of remission) and after the final lapse of state control in 1695? The general point should perhaps be made here, that newspapers have yet to be realistically located at the heart of the structures of print and of metropolitan culture during the late seventeenth and eighteenth centuries and their purposes remain largely misunderstood. It is certainly true that none of the secondary writing on 'shipwrecks' make even a gesture of acknowledgement towards the material published before 1740.[2] It may be that the need to correct this view is behind my choice of subject though I would also admit to an unfocused and rather gloomy interest in the image of the ship stuck fast and breaking up on the rocks at the foot of unidentified cliffs. It could also be said that in opening up the issue of information transfer this section is closer to what is now identified as media history than to established lines of book-trade and bibliographical study.[3]

By 1700 a sophisticated framework for the collection and dispersal of information had been established through the London newspapers. It involved techniques of presentation which were instantly recognisable to readers and allowed individuals to establish a recurrent relationship to what may as well be called public reality. In this sense, people knew what lines of material to expect and where to look for them on the page. Their familiarity allowed the compiler, or 'author', to adopt formulas which themselves carried forward meanings allowing for the representation of events which was both spare and dynamic. Newspaper paragraphs were not sub-literary. In some respects they represented a different level of literary creation; this is sometimes slightingly referred to as 'journalism'. A primary characteristic of newspaper content is its openness. It is the only form of printed text which can effectively convey the linear unfolding of events and it is partly this sense of an endless continuation that gives the coverage of shipping and shipwrecks its particular force.

The content of the London newspapers of the late seventeenth century, as well as newspapers of other periods, is usually portrayed as predominantly political.[4] In fact trade and commerce provided the primary impulse to publication and embedded at the centre of the continuously moving picture were the ships on which the commercial well-being of the nation depended. Within the content of the generalist papers shipping was allied with hard-core information consisting of the regularly updated prices of goods and stocks and of the variable exchange rates. This material had had an independent serial existence since the early seventeenth century while shipping itself had begun to experience a form of specialist recording through *Lloyd's List*, first published in the 1690s.[5] The run, including its brief record of 'Casualties', only survives continuously from the 1740s and this seems to have deterred any systematic analysis of the same material offered through the generalist newspapers.

Ship news was an invariable category of information appearing in every issue of all the main London papers. Even so, the contemporary problems of gathering and checking information, as well as the process of selection, compounded by competing demands for space on the page, made the coverage inherently unstable. Attempting to track the movement of individual vessels across or within the London papers is difficult and time-consuming, though not impossible. The main benefits of the sequential reports are their immediacy and also their specificity. The disbenefit, particularly to those who find quantification the ultimate test of value, is the tendency for the information not to be followed through. Accounts of arrivals and departures which begin in the papers may well have ended elsewhere; in oral or written reports, in a manuscript or printed supplement which has not survived or on the printing office floor, squeezed out of the text by the arrival of new information.[6]

The assembling of the newspaper coverage of the movement of shipping was based on the supply of information which was seldom acknowledged and is therefore largely a matter of inference. Even in the case of the *London Gazette*, the origins of much of the coverage of shipping is hard to pin down. The compilers of the *Gazette* could draw on materials supplied by the network of local officials working in ports all round the country as excise officers or as postmasters, though there is not much evidence that these contacts were systematically exploited.[7] They also had the massive advantage of privileged access to the reports of naval commanders at sea. It was the publication of early and accurate information on the activities of the Royal Navy that gave the *Gazette* part of its edge over commercial rivals.

Some of the compilers of the competing serials may have established personal contacts in the ports who supplied regular information about the movement of ships in return for copies of the paper or even a modest fee. This was an arrangement visible in the newspaper records from the 1750s.[8] On the other hand, both the compilers of the *Gazette* and their commercial rivals published simultaneous reports containing identical information sometimes distinguished only by the choice of words. The clear implication is of a shared source – either a single composite, prepared in London from local information, or a series of locally prepared newsletters available individually to the newspaper printers and compilers. All the London newspapers referred simply to 'Our Port Letters' and in the absence of surviving or identified examples of any such source the nature of the transaction must remain entirely speculative. Working out how the reports of shipping movements, as well as other local events, in Deal, Falmouth, Harwich, Plymouth and elsewhere were packaged and distributed will form part of a more general attempt to reconstruct the information networks of early modern England.

London was the centre for well over half of the national trade and the material published under the general 'London' dateline was compiled from an equally obscure range of sources which related to the commercial activity centred on the Port of London.[9] National and international trade was supported by an intricate network of semi-formal correspondence which could be accessed, to various degrees, by the compilers of the London newspapers. In particular, the merchants on the Royal Exchange provided a target for news-gathering, becoming a generalised reference point for the validation of reports on a wide range of issues including the movement of shipping. At the same time, the walks of the Exchange buzzed with information as ships' captains, travellers and traders of all nationalities passed through London engaged in the endless enterprise of capitalism which was most clearly represented in the developing forms of serial print.[10]

The flow of information on which the newspaper compilers drew extended in all directions and covered vast distances. The existence of a network of nuclear centres of information-gathering and newspaper publication, towns and cities of which London was a major representative, generated a torrent of printed material. Continental and overseas newspapers arrived in London with every mail and were available for translation and inclusion in the locally produced serials of which they formed another, generally unacknowledged part.[11] All these strands are difficult to unravel when the mechanics of the gathering, selection and presentation of news remain below the surface. Even so, the picture of shipping and trade contained in the London papers is dynamic and, as far as the circumstances of the time allowed, comprehensive.

Material flowed into the offices of the newspaper printers and was assembled and redirected by the compilers for whom the latest reports were the most valuable. Ships sailing to and from London were picked up in the coverage attributed to the 'Port Letters' and their progress inward and outward given an erratic existence in print. Outward-bound ships swung out to sea sometimes to reappear in distant locations caught by other sources. If the detail was sometimes blurred, the strands of printed information could enable contemporaries to follow, particularly in the case of East India ships, individual voyages across the world in both directions. Arrival of East Indiamen back in coastal waters, sometimes reported by Pursers put ashore on the South coast and riding flat-out for the Exchange, was followed by publication in at least one of the papers of an exact account of the composition of cargoes. This could be corrected or extended when the ships arrived in the river and subsequently newspaper readers could track the dispersal of the exotic commodities through the London market and become active participants through news reports and advertisements.

In some papers special efforts were made to systematise the reporting of ships and shipping. John Smith of Great Queen Street had a particular interest in the publication of comprehensive commercial information and in his *Currant Intelligence*, which first appeared in February 1680, he offered readers a list 'of all the Merchant Ships that either come in or go out of any Port of the West of England'.[12] His coverage also included the other main ports of the British Isles and while his paper remained in publication it seems, partly at least, to have been compiled from an exclusive correspondence. His later speculation in serial commerce was more landlocked. It was represented by a paper entitled the *Jockie's Intelligence* which offered readers 'weekly advertisements of horses and second-hand coaches'.[13] Other attempts at establishing some control over the coverage of shipping were occasionally promoted in the newspaper press. In 1696 the compiler of the *Old Post Man* stated that 'For the future, there shall be incerted weekly, the names of all Ships Entered Inwards, and of all Ships Cleared out the week past, in the Port of London'.[14] His commitment to this form of commercial information, whatever its source, was suggested in the same issue by the inclusion of ship news from ten separately identified Irish ports.

The attempts at comprehensive coverage were heroic but in the end unsustainable. The machinery of information-gathering was too insecure while the sheer scale and range of the movement of shipping made such sequential reports inescapably impressionistic. The density of movement around the coast of Britain as ships arrived or prepared to disperse for voyages to the distant East or West, to the ports of Europe or the multiple destinations of the British coastal trade, was daunting. A report in the *Post Man* in January 1699 stated,

There are in the *Downs*, 3 Ships bound for the *East Indies*, 7 for *Guinea*, 8 for *Virginia*, 3 for *Barbadoes*, 5 for *Malaga*, 3 for *Lisbon*, 2 for the *Streights*, 2 for *Antego*, 2 for *Barbary*, 2 for *Cape Verd*, 3 for *Ireland*, 1 for *Jamaica* and *Madras*, 1 for *New England*, 2 for *Viara*, 1 for *Alicant*, 1 for *Galicia*, 1 for *Sevil*, besides 12 of His Majestys Ships.[15]

Correspondents in various ports were working at the limits of the possible, listing the ships in sight or speculating about those observed as the weather closed in:

Falmouth. April 26th [1697]. There is now standing at this Port a Fleet of Ships, but the Weather being hazy, we cannot tell their Number, we suppose them to be the Fleet bound for *New-found-land*.[16]

Keeping ahead of the information game involved a willingness on everybody's part to include speculative material. Ships or Fleets which were the subject of a 'hot discourse on the Exchange' were included in the coverage as was information about new arrivals which could only be verified or corrected at a later time.

The level of reporting of ship news was at its peak in wartime. The London papers covered the movement of both the Royal Navy and merchant ships and the strings of names, destinations and commanders which characterised the routine coverage from the main English ports, often reflected the formation of convoys serving a combined military and commercial purpose. Sir George Rook on expeditions to the Mediterranean during the 1690s was invariably accompanied by shoals of merchant ships in both directions. The *London News Letter* carried a report from Deal in April 1696 that on the return of the Admiral 'the crowd of Ships in the *Downs* is so great at present, that it is impossible to particularize any further than that'.[17] The formation of such convoys was an essential preliminary to some voyages in both war and peace when piracy and privateering represented a serious risk. In 1681 the crew of the 'Greyhound' were reported to have refused to sail to Cephalonia without a convoy, had 'arrested' the ship, and caused serious losses to the merchants involved.[18] Royal Navy squadrons, with or without merchant ships, were always on the move. The correspondents associated with the Port Letters from Deal, Portsmouth, Plymouth and Falmouth and elsewhere did their best to fill in the gaps, quizzing captains, crews and passengers of the ships inward, to establish sightings at sea. The packet boats, sailing to and fro on fairly regular timetables particularly between Falmouth and Lisbon, provided useful material. In February 1698 the compiler of *Dawks' Newsletter* included a characteristic report:

Our Port Letters say, That on the 26th past in the morning, the Alliance [a packet running out of Falmouth] saw 5 great Ships about 40 Leagues from the Lizzard, standing S.W. the biggest of which carrying a Flag, they are supposed to be Commander Warrens Squadron bound for India.[19]

Fig. 1. A Storm at Sea. By Wenceslaus Hollar (1665).

Within the lines of serial information about shipping were embedded the elements of shipwreck. The general estimate that about one in ten sea voyages, particularly over distance, ended in disaster seems to be supported in the newspaper reports. As Dr John Wilkinson, in his polemic promoting his cork life-jacket asked in the 1750s, 'what rock, what coast, what sand-bank is not notorious for the destruction of *Englishmen*?'[20] The news reports on shipwreck were generally unembellished but in a short space the information narrative could have a compressed force. The most complete coverage was provided on the Royal Navy through the sources available to the *London Gazette.* In 1694 the paper carried a full account dated from Whitehall 28 March describing the disastrous effects of bad weather (combined with faulty navigation) on the squadron sailing for Gibraltar. The news arrived by an express routed through Cadiz which reported that as the ships were approaching the Straits at about 10.00 a.m. on Sunday morning

There arose a violent Storm, with Thunder, Lightning and a great deal of Rain, the Wind at East and E.N.E. changing afterwards to E.S.E. The storm continued all that Day and the Night following; on *Monday* the 19th, about 5 in the morning, Sir *Francis Wheelers* own Ship, the *Sussex* foundered, he and all his men being lost except two Moors.

Following the report was a list of all the ships with their respective losses and news of the finding of Admiral Wheeler's mangled body.[21]

This sort of detailed account was seldom offered outside the framework of official reporting although an element of drama was often present in even the most prosaic newspaper paragraphs. To some extent, this was generated by the uncertainty of the unfolding narrative in which the outcome of voyages or even the implications of the information published remained in doubt. Among the routine shipping reports which permeated the London newspapers, comments on ships long overdue or on wreckage found but not identified, created an alternative narrative tension. Round-trip voyages to the East Indies and beyond usually took at least 18 months to complete and this timing could be extended to several years. Sometimes, newspaper reports relayed the sort of fragmentary information which must have been continuously buzzing round the Exchange. In January 1679 the letter from Falmouth reported the return of a ship from 'Sally' which on the voyage home had come across the wreck of a ship of about 200 tons. It was a total loss and the only sign of identification was a plank engraved with the name 'Endeavour'.[22] Sometimes the extended delays had a happier outcome. In June 1699 *Dawks'* reported,

Yesterday the Purser of the Chambers Frigat came Post from Deal, and appeared upon Change, bringing the Joyful News of that Ships arrival in the Downes, being very richly Laden from the Indies, she having been out ever since 1695.[23]

The previous year the late arrival of an East Indiaman was said to have surprised the wives of sixteen of the seamen who had married again in the interim ('Always Provided is never at Want' added the news writer sardonically).[24]

Ship news about wrecks outside coastal waters was often hasty and uncertain. In 1698 *Dawks'* reported that, 'Letters from Cadiz say that an English Ship is Run aground near St Lucar, which it is feared is either the Portsmouth Galley, bound for the Indies, or the Neptune Bound for Smyrna.'[25] Information was included in the news as received and the lack of specific detail on the names of ships and masters, usually supplied in the port letters, could hardly be supplemented by struggling compilers with few resources and deadlines to meet. A characteristic combination of specificity and obliquity appeared in the *Post Man* also in 1698.

They write from *Oporto*, that a Ship of Bidiford sprang a leak about 60 leagues from shore whereupon the Seamen and Passengers about 40 in number, quitted the Ship, and betook themselves to a Long Boat, but a Sea breaking over them near *Averrs*, they were all drowned, except 3 Men and a boy.[26]

Ships sailing in and out of English ports were at their most vulnerable at the points of arrival and departure and the compilers of the port letters were caught up in the hurry of events, relaying the earliest information of disaster or expressing local fears as bad weather blew up. The sense of the struggle to make sense of fragmented information appeared in a letter from Falmouth of 16 December 1699 published in the *Post Boy*:

We hear, That a Dutch Ship with Masts bound for Bourdeau is cast away some Miles to the Eastward of this place. 'Tis said also, that a considerable outward bound English Ship is lost to the West-ward of the Manakells, but we do not hear the Names of either, or any other circumstances of them.[27]

Ten days later the *Flying Post* reported under a London dateline,

Beginning of last Week a great quantity of different sorts of Wrecks came ashoar on the Coast of *Cornwall*, a great part of which was *West-India* Commodities, with some Casks of Wine and Brandy: So that its feared more than one or two Merchant Men have been cast away in the late storm on that Coast.[28]

It seems to have been a bad year for coastal shipping and the correspondent from Harwich in November, after reporting a storm which had driven several ships ashore, went on to express 'great pain for the last Fleet of laden Colliers which sailed thence'.[29] Such uncertainties were unavoidable in the newspaper coverage and to some extent they provided a valuable mechanism for securing reader interest. While many wanted hard information on the outcome of voyages, others were probably satisfied with a more generalised and dramatic narrative.

The newspaper reporting of ship news, based on a continuous and multi-directional flow of information, reflected a pattern of shipwreck in line with that established through examination of the more systematic and approachable records of later periods. The months from October to February were the most dangerous and the coasts of England were ringed with black spots where time and again ships went down when returning from or setting out on voyages. The Scilly Isles, said to be mischarted by at least five leagues on all the maps, the Isle of Wight and the channel with

Portland, the rocks just off Falmouth harbour and the Goodwin Sands were routinely identified in the newspaper coverage.[30]

To the general hazards of sea travel (leaks, fire, storms, rocks, defective navigation) all of which were reported in the London news-papers, can be added the interventions of communities living on the coasts in areas where wrecks were common. Sailing along the coast of Norfolk in the 1640s, William Johnson 'saw the ruines of Shipwrack, and the Countrey people enriching themselves with the losses of other men, the worst way of getting in the world.'[31] The possible post-wreck hazards were illustrated in a separately-published narrative of 1684 which described the wreck of the 'President' in Mount Bay in Cornwall on its return from the East Indies.[32] After the two sole survivors had scrambled ashore they were almost immediately knocked on the head by some passing country folk on the look-out for spoils from the ship. The seamen were rescued and the attackers gaoled but there were more problems. 'On the Sunday immediately following, in Sermon-Time, the People of the next Town heard of the Wreck, whereupon with one consent they ran out from their Devotions to the Spoil, leaving the Parson to Preach to the bare Walls.'[33] By the time the East India Company got its representatives into the area the entire cargo, of which the Company's share alone was valued at £100,000, had been stripped.

Materials washed ashore had limited provenance and were eagerly looked for. In December 1700 the compiler of the *Post Man* reported:

Our Port Letters bring little of moment, save only from *Cows*, that several pieces of Callico are daily driven ashoar on that Coast, which is judged to be part of the Cargo of one of the Ships formerly mentioned to be cast away upon that Island. The Goods as fast as they come on shoar are carried away by the Country people, who are in great numbers daily along the Sea side, picking up what they can find.'[34]

The problem of ownership and of confrontation became critical when a ship, such as the 'President', was thrown on shore with its cargo more or less intact. When the 'Peace of Savoy' and another French ship were driven on to Portland beach with their cargoes of brandy and wine respectively the attempt at securing the property had an unfortunate outcome. The local exciseman, Thomas Tod, showed such unusual zeal that he climbed on board too soon and 'was drowned, as he was busying himself about the Wreck.'[35] At least that is what the papers said. A characteristic newspaper narrative drawn from a local report and centred on a wreck was published in August 1698 by Benjamin Harris in the

London Post. It described how, when 'the *Duke of Gloster* run on Shoar off the Isle of *Wight*, the Country-men came aboard, and open one of the Casks, found it filled with Hats, which finding, they threw their old Hats into the Sea and put each a new Hat on their Heads; ...'. The Captain tried to prevent this form of customary self-help and was told ''twas a Wreck, and therefore lawful'. On hearing this he drew his sword and sliced off the ear of one of the boarders. Before things got entirely out of hand, the garrison from Hurst Castle arrived and ejected the country-men.[36]

The treatment of shipwreck within the general coverage of shipping, like other areas of news and information, could be imbued in a small space with humour, tragedy, drama and adventure. The approach could depend on the perceived audience of the individual serial or simply on the character of the source itself. Some of the most striking shipwreck material appeared in verbatim quotation from letters, whether or not intended for public consumption. The *London Gazette*, for all its stifling air of state control, sometimes carried sharply observed eye-witness reports of shipwrecks as well as battles. By printing letters written on board ship, a practice sometimes adopted in the commercial papers, the *Gazette* regularly offered a kind of immediacy not often found elsewhere. The wreck of the 'Association' and the drowning of Admiral Sir Cloudesly Shovell on the rocks which surrounded the Scillies in October 1707 was the subject of one such news report. The narrative of events was given in two letters, the first 'From on Board the *Royal Anne* at Spithead, October 25.' The tone is clear, the information precise and the scene from the 'Royal Anne' dramatic.

In the afternoon Sir Cloudesly Shovell brought to, and lay by, having very fresh Gales at S.S.W. hazey weather. At Six at Night he made the Signal for sailing. We made Sail under our Courses. Soon after several Ships made signal of Danger, as did Sir Cloudesly himself. The Royal Anne that was not then half a Mile to Windward of him, saw several Breaches, and, soon after the Rocks above Water: Upon one of which she saw the Association strike, and in less than two Minutes disappear. The Royal Anne was saved by the great Presence of Mind both in Officers and Men, who in a Minute's time set her Top-sails, one of the Rocks not being a Ship's Length to Leeward of her, on which Sir Cloudesly was lost, ...[37]

This was followed in the same issue by a further dramatic narrative in a letter from Captain Percy, commander of a fireship called the 'Firebrand'. The ship actually struck the rocks but the captain managed, by 'backing her Fore-sail', to drive off only to have the vessel founder in ten fathoms shortly after. Captain and crew were all saved while none of the hundreds of men on the 'Association' survived.[38]

Death by misadventure through shipwreck was not limited to sea travel and the London papers of the late seventeenth century carried a litany of reports of wrecks and accidents taking place in harbours and inland waterways. In the 1750s Wilkinson reckoned that about 300 people a year drowned in English rivers, of whom well over a half were lost in the Thames.[39] The passenger boats sailing up and down the river often smashed into London Bridge and were particularly vulnerable to winter weather. In February 1698 the *Post Man* reported a series of fatal accidents on the river of which the most serious involved a 'tilt-boat' sailing up from Gravesend with 60 passengers. Five miles into the journey 'the Wind blowing very high, the Boat in Tacking about overset, whereby all the Passengers were drowned except 7, who were saved by a man of wars boat, ...'.[40] According to the papers, bodies were still being taken out of the water five months later.[41]

As the volume of London-centred maritime commerce accelerated during the later seventeenth century the range of printed material concerned with ships and shipwreck broadened out. The newspapers, compiled by printers and a variety of mainly unknown individuals on the fringes of the book trade, provided a point of intersection for information concerned with wrecks both in terms of prevention and speculation. The pragmatic interest of the state was represented by the sequence of notices from Trinity House which radiated out from the *Gazette* and located hazards, including submerged wrecks, and gave precise details of the position of marker buoys and lights.[42] These seem to have been intended for use, though whether masters of ships relied on the newspapers seems doubtful. However, the framework for much of the news and advertising concerned with shipwreck was inescapably commercial as individuals, usually with the support of Letters Patent, struggled to cash in on ship-related inventions. Promotional material appeared as separate publications (broadsides, pamphlets and handbills) but it was also manifested in the columns of the London newspapers. Devices for making fresh water out of salt, for sheathing ships in milled lead or for inflatable life-preservers were marketed through the serials. A characteristic speculator who contributed to the upswing in the volume of post-licence print was George Oldner. He received a patent for an 'Invention to Preserve Ships from Foundring or Sinking at Sea &c.'.[43] While attempting to keep the details of his invention secret (it seems to have been some sort of bilge pump) he also tried to raise £60,000 in shares. It is hard to judge the substance of his claims which were attacked as having 'a Monstrous and Unaccountable Air of Whimsie and Confidence'.[44] Oldner may have been the sort of speculator that Daniel Defoe was keen to expose in his *Essay upon Projects* in 1697.

Perhaps the most striking area of wreck-centred speculation manifested in the newspapers concerned the various approaches to salvage. With ships going down with valuable cargoes on a regular basis the opportunities for a speculative profit must have looked good. This was particularly the case following the remarkable success of Sir William Phips in the mid-1680s in fishing up silver from a Spanish galleon wrecked in the West Indies 40 years before.[45] The salvage of £200,000-worth of coins was against all the odds. As Defoe wrote, 'Bless us! that Folks should go Three thousand Miles to Angle in the open Sea for Pieces of Eight! Why they wou'd have made Ballads of it'.[46] The response to such underwater possibilities was reflected in the papers. In the *Post Boy* in June 1695 it was reported that

'On *Saturday* a new invented Diving Engine, contrived by Mr. *John Stephens* and Mr. *Martin Hopkins*, both of *Topsham* in Devon, was experienced in the River *Thames* near *Blackwal*, where the former remained 4 Fathom under water for the space of half an hour, and there danced, sung, and answered several Questions through the Pipes that reached into the Boat, and was so active that he could do any Business that reason can require to the great satisfaction of a numerous resort of Spectators ...'[47]

The practical application to which such inventions could be applied were also given coverage in the newspapers. At the time of the Darien expedition in Central America, some mouth-watering reports appeared. In *Dawks' Newsletter* in April 1699, a paragraph stated that letters had been received from Captain Richard Long, a Quaker, then in the vicinity of Panama, and that

When these Letters came away, Capt. Long was then preparing to go to Fish on two considerable Plate Wrecks, lost near the said Island [not identified]; for the use of his Grace the Duke of Schomberg, and Company: one of these Wrecks has in her 4 Millions of Treasure, and according to what he writes he did not doubt but to be able to fish up that Silver in a short time.[48]

The rustle of share certificates is almost audible. Eight months later, optimistic reports of progress were appearing in the papers, though the total estimated value of the cargo had gone down to £400,000. Reports of salvage were usually more prosaic and concerned the retrieval of guns and other materials from ships sunk in, or close to, English harbours.

Fig.2. An eighteenth-century diving-bell.

Print was the medium for projecting these enterprises and members of the London book trade were also active in speculating, usually with the aid of strings of newspaper advertisements, in areas of wreck-related publication. The strand of non-cartographic material concerned with navigation and the practice of seamanship, the anti-wreck output of the trade, was dominated in mid-century by William Fisher and subsequently by Richard Mount, bookseller on Tower Hill, the traditional meeting point for sailors.[49] In the main, this was technical and mathematical in character and included a few publications which by the 1690s had been in print for a century or more. Mount's publications figured extensively in the papers from the mid-1690s and they contributed to the training in the arts of the sea that led some reports to refer to skilled navigators as 'artists'.

Through the news and advertising carried by the London papers of the later seventeenth century, readers were kept informed of the movement of ships and of the efforts to secure or exploit the seagoing traffic on which the wealth of the community depended. Shipwreck, like crime, sounded a discordant note within the narrative of events providing material which was both gripping and threatening. Its appeal could carry the shipwreck narrative into a separate existence in the books and pamphlets which centred on these events and the subsequent, usually dire, experiences of the survivors. The volume of such material was not great, and publication usually took the form of small-format books or pamphlets. General accounts of voyages and travels in which multiple shipwrecks occurred were in some respects to one side of this literature. In *The History of the Voyages and Travels of Capt. Nathaniel Uring*, published in 1722, a good deal of space was devoted to wrecks. For example, his record of a voyage from Madeira to Jamaica included:

an Account of the Author being cast away upon a Reef of Rocks near some small desart Island, about Twenty five Leagues from the main Land; with a Relation of the Loss of his Boat, and what Difficulties he met with in getting from thence. His making a Raft or Float with the Ships Masts and Yards, on which he carried most part of the Goods and Provisions saved out of the Wreck to Honduras; ...[50]

This is a shipwreck narrative. But overall it forms part of a much more pragmatic work of autobiography and general travel, 'Very useful for Masters of Ships that use the *Leeward* Island Trade or *Jamaica*', and an integral part of the book was concerned with promoting a settlement in the West Indies.[51]

The works briefly discussed here were focused on the shipwreck itself and the immediate aftermath, suggesting how in the period up to about 1720 such experiences were represented and marketed in print. The narratives had a generic relationship to the continuous newspaper coverage with which they overlapped. The problem facing the authors and publishers of the one-off accounts in book or pamphlet form was of credibility. The issues of credit and fixity in relation to print have recently become the subject of some close analysis.[52] In the news serial the validation of all forms of content, including accounts of shipwrecks, took an unusual form.

Newspapers were not legitimised by association with the respectable book trade, far from it, nor was there a circle of readers whose cultural status in some way guaranteed the quality of their content. Reports were not identified with named individuals, either as eye-witnesses or as writers. The newspaper was in some respects a self-validating mechanism underwritten by the process of serial publication and a relationship to an almost universal system of intelligence. To some extent, it was market forces, the constant possibility of exposure by rival publications or by readers, that underpinned the material which they contained. The newspapers at the end of the seventeenth century dealt in the kind of updated detail that had to be seen to work in relation to the world (mainly that of business) as well as to fit in with what was identified as a generalised narrative of events. This did not mean that everything they contained was either accurate or true. But it can be said that in relation to ships and shipwrecks they offered, within the parameters of the possible, a reliable and comprehensive coverage. Compilers were eager to expose the occasional attempts to insert false information, sometimes to influence the price of stocks, and if initial reports were mistaken the truth was likely to emerge in the end.

This did not apply to one-off publications dealing with travel in general or shipwreck in particular. Partly because of the sensational and unfamiliar subjects dealt with in the narratives, it was customary to offer readers an apparatus by which some part at least of the circumstances described could be tested. Eyewitnesses were listed or access to documentary material offered to confirm the information contained in the text. Even William Johnson who, by the time of publishing his account of shipwreck on the coast of Norway, was a chaplain to Charles II, ended his graphic description with an authenticating list of participants. These included the owners and crew of the 'William and John' of Ipswich and extended to 'Two Boyes'. His list ended 'And others whose Names I cannot remember; most of these are alive, and can testify these sad things, and some are faln asleep.'[53]

Shipwreck narratives, like accounts of serious crime, were often published in the context of providential interventions. Here again personal testimony provided an appropriate counterpoint, bolstering the reader's confidence in the truth of the stories of salvation and destruction at sea. However, shipwreck material was not uniform in either its presentation or its intent. The narrative provided a vehicle through which a number of different agendas, ideological and commercial, could be followed. The shipwreck entered the market from several directions, slotting into the output of individual booksellers and printers whose publications reflected wide disparities in approach. The way in which the variables in this micro-area of print were formulated, can be seen in the narratives issued by Dorman Newman and Nathaniel Crouch. Both worked for a time in Cheapside, adjacent to Grocer's Hall, both developed an interest in topical material, including newspapers, and both were wholesale distributors of patent medicines. Neither Newman nor Crouch had a special interest in ships or shipwrecks but they each published distinct versions of this narrative form.

During the 1670s Newman's publications were dominated by religious material, in particular by the works of nonconformist ministers. His catalogue, apparently issued in the mid-1670s, ended with a full-page notice of a new translation of the Psalms, recommended by 26 ministers, including Edmund Calamy and James Janeway, and sold by Newman for $\frac{1}{4}d$.[54] It was this background that provided the setting for publication of what is generally taken to be the first compilation of shipwreck narratives. Newman's catalogue was itself issued with copies of *Mr. James Janeway's Legacy to his Friends Containing Twenty Seven Famous Instances of Gods Providence in and about Sea Dangers and Deliverances* (1675). By the time it appeared Janeway was dead. He was said to have collected the narratives 'but had not had time to polish and adorn them in his sweet and taking Style, as he did other things'.[55] Publication was carried on by John Ryther, minister of the seafaring parish of Wapping, who clearly expressed the purpose of the collection in his letter to the reader. 'Here thou mayst see the prevailing Power of Prayer, the Wonder-working Power of God, the unspeakable Bowels and tender Mercies of God, to poor Perishing, Sinking, Drowning, Starving dying Men; ...' As in the case of Johnson's *Deus Nobiscum*, the text was accompanied by a long sermon and was rounded off with some solid 'Applications'.

Shipwrecks were not the only sea dangers described. Ryther included a long narrative based on a pamphlet published in 1631 which outlined the experiences of a group of Englishmen left behind in Greenland by mistake and forced to overwinter in awful conditions.[56] Many of the episodes did involve wrecks, often in ships from or on the way to New England, and most were dated. The chronology came close to the date of publication and in spite of the polemical intention the narratives were plain and effective. 'In the month of *November* 1669, the *Ship* Prosperous of *Bristol*, being bound for *Galloway* in *Ireland*, but was forced into *Bruts-Bay* in *Cornwal*, where the Ship broke in pieces, ...'[57] This sounds like news, its truth in some respects supported by the detail offered and its recognisable form. Six people were drowned in the wreck and only John Denny, a skinner from Bristol, was washed ashore alive. Like most of the accounts, this one ended 'the said *Denny* is now well and liveth at *Bristol*. This my Author had from *John Denny's* own mouth.' Only here and there do elements of the miraculous crop up, as when an old man lashed to a main hatch after two days adrift was confronted by 'the Devil assuming a Mair-maid' and was finally rescued through the dream of a cabin boy.[58] Strange things happen at sea. The collection remained popular and was republished in 1708 as *A Token for Mariners* which brought it into line with Janeway's better known work *A Token for Children* suggesting a semi-educational status shared with the records of crime.[59]

Janeway fitted easily into Newman's list. Shipwrecks figured rather differently in the output of Nathaniel Crouch. Although still including a strong element of 'Divinity' in his catalogue in the 1690s he was already putting his name, initials at least, to more secular material in the 1670s. The publication, which suggests an alternative approach in the earlier period and which appeared shortly after the second edition of Johnson (1672) and shortly before the Janeway collection, has been attributed to Richard Head. *The Western Wonder: Or, O Brazeel* (1674) inverted the conventional components of the shipwreck narrative satirising the elements of providential intervention, the use of prayer, the language of seamen ('A language *like* a Storm to be abhor'd') and even the usual tropes of description.[60] The approach is very like that of the 'Poor Robin' material attributed to Head's biographer William Winstanley and adopted in several topical–satirical news serials published from the late 1670s.[61] Head himself shared the fate of the sailor–poet William Falconer and was drowned during a sea voyage.[62]

By the 1690s Crouch was identified with an alternative line of populist publication in which shipwreck narratives can also be located. His publishing output included a variety of cheap duodecimos, many of them formed by boiling down the contents of substantial folios beyond the financial reach, as well as the interest, of many potential purchasers. He himself wrote under the pseudonym of Richard or Robert Burton (R. B.) and as John Dunton remarked, '[h]e has melted down the best of our English histories into twelve penny books, which are filled with wonders rarities and curiosities; for you must know his title-pages are a little swelling.'[63] Among his prolix publications was *Memorable Accidents, and Unheard of Transactions Containing an Account of several Strange Events* ... (1693), a translation from the French. It started with a shipwreck and included several others in the course of the book. The narratives were lively enough and the detailed account of a ship being dashed to pieces near the Cape of Good Hope probably played its part in satisfying reader demand for excitement.[64] Crouch does not seem to have had any more to do with the form in this sort of 'prodigy' setting. However, he may have had an interest in a print containing a 'view of a 3rd Rate Man of War at Anchor, shewing all the Rigging and parts of the Hull, with Explanations of the same'. This was advertised in the *Post Man* in November 1707 shortly after the wreck of the 'Association'.[65]

The final example of the relationship between the form and character of the shipwreck narrative and the London book trade involves the accounts of the wreck of the 'Nottingham Galley' which went down on the rocks of Boon Island off the coast of New England in December 1710. The interest of the narrative for the post-licence readership lay in the sufferings of the survivors on a barren outcrop in sight of land and particularly in their recourse to cannibalism.[66] The first account was compiled by the Captain soon after the rescue and was apparently published cheaply in Philadelphia and Scotland before appearing in London. Here it formed part of the output of John Dutton working from premises in 'New Fleetstreet'.[67]

Dutton specialised in the publication of topical broadsides and cheap pamphlets and through this output he seems to have established some business links with James Read, a printer in Whitefriars. Read later owned and printed a long-running weekly newspaper with his name in the masthead and among his earlier topical publications was *Providence Display'd: Or, a very Surprizing Account of One Mr. Alexander Selkirk* (1712).[68] Dutton was one of a number of London publishers who issued eight-page chapbooks with an elaborate content trailer on the title, a large woodcut engraving and a licensing statement. This latter item, a hangover from before 1695, may have been used to give an illusion of authority to the cheap, topical items. It was in this form that Dutton published *A Sad and Deplorable, but True Account of the Dreadful Hardships and Sufferings of Capt. John Dean, and his Company on Board the Nottingham Galley ...* (1711). Above a large woodcut of a ship in sail the more appealing elements of the content were laid out:

Showing how they liv'd near a Month upon the Rock, in bitter Frost and Snow, some losing their Feet, Toes, Nails, with the use of their Limbs, and some their Lives: Also, how, having no Food, they were fain to Feed upon the Dead Bodies, which being all Consum'd, they were going to cast Lots which shou'd be next Devour'd ...

The long rehearsal ended in the usual way, 'This Account being Attested by the Captain's own Hand, and two others, and very well known by most Merchants upon the *Royal Exchange*.' The narrative contained a favourable account of the Captain's behaviour and some modest criticism of the crew who were said to have become hard to control after eating the carpenter.

   This narrative did not pass unchallenged. At some time during 1711 a response was drawn up by members of the crew launching a violent attack on Dean and his associates.[69] It was sold by Sarah Popping at the Raven in St Paul's Churchyard who, like Newman, was later to develop an interest in newspapers and whose links to nonconformity were personal as well as commercial. In the narrative Dean was accused of attempting an insurance scam intending from the first to sink the 'Nottingham Galley'. Such strategies sometimes surfaced in the advertising columns of the newspapers of the late seventeenth century, as investors struggled to combat this damaging form of commercial fraud. In the case of the 'Nottingham Galley' the attack on the captain went further. He was said to have suggested eating the carpenter and his behaviour was reviled even after the rescue. He 'returned with the Dog to his Vomit', barbarously telling the local children that 'he would have made a Frigasy of them if he had had 'em in *Boon Island*.'[70] The long narrative was followed by a series of sworn statements made in New England and in London by Christopher Langman, the mate, and two others. The controversy was personal and professional but through the public medium of print it became in a more general way part of the literature of shipwreck.

While the shipwreck did not have a very high profile within the general output of the trade, it was always present. The subject had a strongly practical application for a broad cross-section of readers. As information, it had a crucial impact on the circles of people living and working in London whose livelihoods were closely dependent on the successful completion of long- and short-distance voyages. Travellers were almost certain at some time to take to the water, an experience which was said to be 'almost universally disliked',[71] and their fears must have been fed by the continuous flow of material available in print which carried its own awful warnings. At the same time, the shipwreck and its aftermath was deeply embedded in the national psyche. The subject was always available as a mechanism for the development of ideas which fitted the cultural preoccupations of society at different social levels. In the 1720s wrecks were routinely integrated into the forms of polite fiction in which luscious and romantic events, as well as pseudo-reality and satire, formed the main lines of appeal.[72] The continued use of sea phrases (including 'shipwreck' itself which gives the title of this piece a slightly enigmatic meaning) as well as the long-running interest in the fate of the 'Titanic', underlines the deep-seated nature of its cultural existence. Shipwreck and survival have always worked as an effective metaphor for life,[73] and the printed representations of the event resonated with readers as ships and crews went down into 'David Jones, his locker'.

References

1. Some of the general remarks about ships and shipwrecks are based on material in Peter Earle, *Sailors; English Merchant Seamen, 1650–1775* (London: Methuen, 1998).

2. The way in which print worked in the construction of English society during the seventeenth and eighteenth centuries has not yet registered in the output of most contemporary historians. The lively and informative studies produced by, for example, Peter Earle and Paul Langford, make no reference to newspapers or other serials as mechanisms for cultural formation and the material they contained is as yet largely unexplored.

3. For an indication of developments in this area see material published in the journal *Media History*.

4. For examples of recent work in which the newspaper is identified with party political activity see Robert Harris, *A Patriot Press; National Politics and the London Press in the 1740s* (Oxford: Clarendon Press, 1993) and Hannah Barker, *Newspapers, Politics and Public Opinion in Late Eighteenth Century England* (Oxford: Clarendon Press, 1998).

5. John McCusker and C. Gravesteijn, *The Beginnings of Commercial and Financial Journalism* (Amsterdam: NEHA, 1991). Includes an international bibliography of commercial serials.

6. The problem of absent sources is compounded in relation to the tri-weeklies published after 1695. The compilers of most or all of these papers published regular supplements, in print or manuscript, of which very few are held in the main newspaper collections.

7. For the information networks centred on government offices see Peter Fraser, *The Intelligence of the Secretaries of State & their Monopoly of Licensed News, 1660–1688* (Cambridge: University Press, 1956).

8. Michael Harris, *London Newspapers in the Age of Walpole* (London and Toronto: Associated University Presses, 1987), p.157.

9. The purpose of the 'London' sub-head is not always clear. The Port Letters were sometimes lumped here rather than placed under separate datelines and its use may have related to the editorial process.

10. Michael Harris, 'Exchanging Information: Print and Business at the Royal Exchange in the Late Seventeenth Century' in Ann Saunders, ed., *The Royal Exchange* (London: London Topographical Society, 1997).

11. For the secondary distribution of foreign newspapers round the London coffee houses see Michael Harris, 'Newspaper Distribution during Queen Anne's reign' in *Studies in the Book Trade* (Oxford: Oxford Bibliographical Society, 1975).

12. *Current Intelligence*, 3 Saturday 21 February 1680. Cited in James Sutherland, *The Restoration Newspaper and its Development* (Cambridge: University Press, 1986), p.114. Smith's name was added to the title from the tenth issue (Tuesday 16 March) to combat a rival paper using the original title.

13. Carolyn Nelson and Matthew Seccombe, *British Newspapers and Periodicals, 1641–1700* (New York: Modern Language Association of America, 1987), entry 207.

14. *Old Post Man* 4 Thursday 2 July 1696.

15. *Post Man* 561 Thursday 12 January 1699.

16. *Post Boy* 310 Saturday 1 May 1697.

17. *London News-Letter* 1 Wednesday 29 April 1696. This convoy could be followed through the *Gazette* to the Isle of Wight and on to the Lizard before disappearing out to sea.

18. *True Protestant Mercury* 80 Wednesday 12 October 1698.

19. *Dawks' News Letter* 411 [Thursday] 2 February 1699.

20. John Wilkinson M.D., *Tutamen Nauticum: Or, the Seaman's Preservation from Shipwreck, Diseases, and Other Calamities Incident to Mariners* (London: 2nd ed., 1763), p.2.

21. *London Gazette* 2961 Thursday 29 March 1694.

22. *London Gazette* 1370 Monday 6 January 1679.

23. *Dawks' News Letter* [465 Thursday] 8 June 1699.

24. *Dawks' News Letter* 362 [Tuesday] 11 October 1698.

25. *Dawks' News Letter* 372 [Thursday] 3 November 1698.

26. *Post Man* 418 Saturday 29 June 1698.

27. *Post Boy* [721] Saturday 16 December 1699.

28. *Flying Post* 722 Tuesday 26 December 1699.

29. *Flying Post* 707 Tuesday 21 November 1699.

30. This was identified in a separately published broadside. *An Advertisement, Necessary to be Observed in the Navigation Up and Down the Channel of England. Communicated by a Fellow of the Royal Society* (London: 1701). The unidentified author wrote, 'For several Years last past it has been Observed that many Ships bound up the Channel,

have by mistake fallen to the Northward of *Scilly*, and run up the *Bristol Channel* or *Severn Sea*, not without great Danger, and the Loss of many of them. The Reason of it is, without dispute, from the Change of the Variation of the Compass, and the Latitude of the *Lizard* and *Scilly*, laid down too far Northerly by near 5 Leagues....'

31.   William Johnson, *Deus Nobiscum. A Sermon Preached upon a Great Deliverance at Sea* (London: 1664), pp.123–4.

32.   William Smith and John Harshfield, *A Full Account of the late Ship-wreck of the Ship Called The President* (London: 1684). Smith and Harshfield were the sole survivors.

33.   *Ibid.*, p.8.

34.   *Post Man* 847 Thursday 26 December 1700.

35.   *Post Man* 550 Thursday 15 December 1698.

36.   *London Post* 36 Monday 28 August 1699.

37.   *London Gazette* 4380 Monday 3 November 1707. Unaccountably none of the commercial tri-weeklies covering this date are present in the Burney Collection in the British Library nor are they listed in other locations.

38.   *Ibid.* There is no reference to the supposed murder of Shovell by a country woman finding him still alive on shore.

39.   Wilkinson, *Tutamen Nauticum*, 54.

40.   *Post Man* 421 Saturday 5 February 1698.

41.   *Dawks' News Letter* 281 [Tuesday] 5 April 1698.

42.   Examples of notices locating a wreck hazard and announcing the replacement of a lighthouse appear in *London Gazette* 2624 Monday 5 January 1691; 2742 Monday 22 February 1691.

43.   The material published by Oldner took a variety of forms and was consistently enigmatic. For example, *Mr. George Oldner's Invention to Preserve Ships from Foundring, or Sinking, at Sea, &c. Experimented and Approv'd and Now Proposed for the Universal Good of All Nations Concern'd in Navigation as Appears by the Following Proposal* (London: 1698).

44.   *An Epistle to a Member of Parliament, Concerning Mr. George Oldner's Invention to Preserve Ships from Foundring or Sinking at Sea* (London: 1699), p.3.

45.   This is the subject of Peter Earle's gripping study *The Wreck of the Almiranta* (London: Macmillan, 1979).

46.   Daniel Defoe, *An Essay upon Projects* (London: 1697), p.15. Cited in Earle, *Almiranta*, p.11.

47.   *Post Boy* 20 Tuesday 25 June 1695.

48.   *Dawks' News Letter* [444 Thursday] 20 April 1699.

49.   Thomas R. Adams, *The Non-Cartographical Maritime Works Published by Mount and Page* (London: Occasional Publications of the Bibliographical Society, 1, 1985).

50.   *A History of the Voyages and Travels of Capt. Nathaniel Uring* (London: 2nd ed., 1727), index entry, np. Uring claimed in the narrative to be related to Admiral Sir Cloudesly Shovell, pp.83, 101.

51.   Integral with the book but with a separate title-page dated 1725 is *A Relation of the Late Intended Settlement of the Islands of St. Lucia and St. Vincent, in America; In Right of the Duke of Montagu, and Under His Grace's Direction and Orders, in the Year 1722.*

52.   An extended treatment of the historical process by which the validity of print was challenged and partly secured in relation to scientific texts during the later seventeenth century appears in Adrian Johns, *The Nature of the Book* (Chicago: University of Chicago Press, 1998).

53. Johnson, *Deus Nobiscum*, pp.155–6. The information validating the text is indicated in the title.

54. The catalogue is conventionally laid out according to the sizes of the books published and the translation of the Psalms fills the final page, A8v.

55. Janeway, *Providence*, 'Epistle to the Reader', np.

56. The original account of this unintentional arctic expedition was entirely suitable for Janeway's purpose. *God's Power and Providence: Shewed In the Miraculous Preservation and Deliverance of eight Englishmen, left by mischance in Green-land Anno 1630. nine moneths and twelve dayes ... Faithfully reported by Edward Pelham, one of the eight men aforesaid* (London: 1631). Janeway, *Providence*, pp.56–72.

57. *Ibid.*, pp.43–4.

58. *Ibid.*, pp.53–6.

59. The value of trial reports as an aid to teaching children to read appears in occasional advertisements for this material in the late seventeenth century. *A Token for Mariners* (London: 1708) was said on the title to be 'Much Enlarg'd, with the Addition of many New Relations; Mostly Attested by the Persons themselves.' It included *The Seaman's Preacher* and *Prayers for Seamen on all Occasions*.

60. The tone of ironic parody was set in the opening lines, 'New Discoveries of late, are as much admired as Miracles of old, and as dificulty believed, notwithstanding the variety of apparent proofs which demonstrate their undoubted Verity; ...'. The reference to sailors' language appears in the poem 'A great Sea-storm', pp.16–20. An early attempt to systematise the jargon of seamen appeared in Nathaniel Botelier, *Coloquia Maritima: or, Sea-Dialogues* (London: 1688) which included 'A Dictionary, or Explanation of the Names of all Parts of a Ship; Sea-Phrases, or Words of Art used at Sea'.

61. *Poor Robin's Intelligence* (1676–77), subsequently revived and reconstituted under this and related titles. For the attribution of authorship see the *Dictionary of National Biography* (*DNB*), entry for William Winstanley (1628?–1698).

62. *DNB*, entry for Richard Head (1637?–1686?).

63. John Dunton, *Life and Errors* (London: 1705). *DNB*, entry for Robert or Richard Burton (1632?–1725?).

64. The opening narrative was headed simply 'The Shipwrack' and was taken from 'Father Tachard's Voyage to the Kingdom of Siam' begun in 1684, *Accidents*, pp.1–10.

65. *Post Man* 1854 Thursday 27 November 1707. It was 'sold by Mr Crouch in the Poultry, and other Print-sellers of London and Westminster' at one shilling.

66. The general interest in cannibalism appeared in the long-running interest in the events arising from the wreck of the Luxborough in 1727. The circumstances were first outlined in the newspapers at the time of the wreck, a serial narrative was published by the carpenter in 1745 and a final account offered by the son of the Captain in 1787. Information about the earlier publications as well as extracts from the papers appeared in William Boys, *An Account of the Luxborough Galley, By Fire, On Her Voyage from Jamaica to London; with the Sufferings of Her Crew* (1787). For some speculation on the attitude to cannibalism see Margarette Lincoln, 'Shipwreck Narratives of the Eighteenth and Early Nineteenth Century: Indicators of Culture and Identity', *British Journal for Eighteenth-Century Studies*, 20, 2 (Autumn 1997), pp.167–9.

67. This was the only address to appear on the surviving remnants of his large-scale output of single-sheets and chapbooks. Much of it had a strong topical appeal and was presumably sold mainly by the hawkers. For example, *A Warning to London: a Full*

and True Account of a Letter Sent Last Night to Mr. Dodson Discovering a Most Horrid Conspiracy for Setting Fire to London-Bridge, where the Dreadful Fire of London Began (London: 1713).

68.   The link between Read and Dutton is suggested by the single-leaf item cited above (note 66) which was printed by Dutton and has a fragment of a printers' proof by Read on the verso (ESTC on-line).

69.   *A True Account of the Voyage of the Nottingham-Galley of London, John Dean Commander, from the River Thames to New-England* (London: 1711). The title-page referred to 'the Falsehoods of the Captain's Narrative' as well as to the cannibalism and wonderful delivery and ended 'the whole attested upon Oath, by Christopher Langman, Mate; Nicholas Mellen, Boatswain; and George White, Sailor in the said Ship'.

70.   *True Account*, p.24.

71.   Wilkinson, *Tutamen Nauticum*, 3, p.55.

72.   Penelope Aubin, *The Noble Savages: Or, the Lives and Adventures of Two Lords and Ladies, who were Shipwreck'd and Cast upon a Desolate Island near the East-Indies, in the Year 1710* (London: 1722).

73.   See, for example, the use of shipwreck as an image by the poet Samuel Taylor Coleridge, cited in Richard Holmes, *Coleridge: Darker Reflections* (London: Harper Collins, 1998), p.181.

The Grand Tour

JEREMY BLACK

PROTRACTED TRAVEL for pleasure was not unknown in classical and medieval times, but it developed greatly in the sixteenth, seventeenth and eighteenth centuries, becoming part of the ideal education of the social élite, as well as an important source of descriptive and imaginative literature. As tourism developed, its patterns became more regular and the assumptions about where a tourist should go became more predictable. Literary conventions were also established. The term the Grand Tour reflects a later sense that this was an ideal period of the fusion of tourism and social status, as well as a contemporary desire to distinguish protracted and wide-ranging tourism from shorter trips. Although an increasing number of women travelled, usually in male company, tourism was largely the prerogative of the adult male, and, in particular, of the young man in his late teens. In the absence of facilities for mass transport and of paid holidays, tourism was costly and a minority activity. The average Grand Tour lasted longer than a year.[1]

This, at once, however, introduces a variance with the literary sources because the majority of travel accounts were not by aristocrats, and this was even more the case as far as lengthy and coherent manuscript journals and published literature were concerned. Authorship was a social construction. It was not unknown for an aristocrat to offer details of his breakfasts or accommodation, and several aristocrats did publish travel accounts. These included *Letters from Italy* (1776) by Lady Anna Miller, *A Journey through the Crimea to Constantinople* (1789) by Lady Elizabeth Craven, and *A Tour through part of France* (1789) by John Villiers, later 3rd Earl of Clarendon.

Nevertheless those who were termed 'brawny beef-eating barons' by the long-serving envoy in Vienna Robert Murray Keith , or called 'Jolly-boys' by the 'bearleader' (travelling tutor) Robert Wharton did not often leave accounts, certainly seldom published them, but the 'bearleaders', who came from a different social background, often published. Their works included Patrick Brydone's *A Tour through Sicily and Malta* (1775), William Coxe's *Travels into Poland, Russia, Sweden, and Denmark*

(1784–90) and *Travels in Switzerland* (1789), and John Moore's *A View of Society and Manners in France, Switzerland and Germany* (1779) and *A View of Society and Manners in Italy* (1781). In some respects, travel literature paralleled the position in general fiction, with Henry Fielding, Samuel Richardson and Jane Austen writing about their social (but not moral) betters. In this respect, as in many others, the writer Horace Walpole, 4th Earl of Orford, was a maverick.

Differences in social position can be seen in comments on the mechanics of travel. Guidebooks tended to praise public transport, but it is doubtful if many wealthy tourists wished to spend several days in a confined space practising their schoolboy French with strangers. In his *Letters to a Young Gentleman on his setting out for France* (London, 1784) John Andrews advised travelling:

in a public vehicle, where he might have a chance of conversing with a diversity of characters ... People that meet on a travelling party, being usually total strangers to each other, and meeting together for the first and last time, are not fettered by any apprehensions of what may happen from the discourse that passes among them: they indulge themselves without any restraint, and speak of men and things with a latitude and freedom, which they would not dare to use elsewhere'.[2]

The Grand Tour is commonly associated with aristocratic British travellers, more particularly with the eighteenth century,[3] but it was not restricted to the British. Throughout Europe members of the élite travelled for pleasure. The most popular destinations were France, which meant Paris, and Italy. There was no cult of the countryside: tourists travelled as rapidly as possible between major cities, and regarded mountains with horror not joy. The contrast with nineteenth-century tourism was dated from Romanticism and not earlier. The 'pre-Romanticism' that encouraged a response to landscape was more literary in location than a description of élite views, certainly than those of the 'brawny beef-eating barons'. The Italian cities offered pleasure (Venice), Classical antiquity (Rome), Renaissance architecture (Florence), the splendours of Baroque culture (Rome and Venice), opera (Milan and Naples), and warm weather (Naples). Once tourism had become fashionable, increasing numbers travelled, a growth interrupted only by periods of war, when journeys, although not impossible, were made more dangerous or inconvenient by increased disruption and lawlessness.

Even in Britain there were appreciable numbers of foreign tourists, although it is not easy to establish exact numbers. Neither the British nor

Fig.1. The Arrival of a Young Traveller and his Suite during the Carnival in the Piazza di Spagna, Rome by David Allan (1744-96). Allan, a Scot, worked in Rome from 1764 until the late 1770s.

the French government kept accurate records of travellers between their countries. It is worth considering the foreign response to Britain as a form of 'control' experiment on British tourism abroad. American and German travellers to Britain are well represented by William Sachse's *The Colonial American in Britain* (Madison, Wisconsin, 1956), W. D. Robson Scott's *German Travellers in England 1400–1800* (Oxford, 1953), and M. C. Spieckermann *et al.* (eds), *"Der curieuse Passagier": deutsche Englandreise des achtzehnten Jahrhunderts als Vermittler kultureller und technologischer Anregungen* (Heidelberg, 1983); but no comparable work pulls together other European travellers to Britain, and we have to turn to such earlier works as P. Kalm, *Account of a Visit to England* (New York, 1892); C. de Saussure, *A Foreign View of England in the Reign of George II* (London, 1902); F. de la Rochefoucauld, *A Frenchman in England, 1784* (Cambridge, 1933); Casanova, *Memoirs* (London, 1940); and H. Monod-Cassidy (ed.), Jerome Lalande, *Journal d'un voyage en Angleterre 1763* (Oxford, 1980).

In recent years, a number of important accounts have appeared. Count Karl von Zinzendorf, who travelled widely in Europe, was especially interested in technological developments. Although his lengthy description of his extensive travels remains unpublished in the Haus-, Hof-, und Staatsarchiv in Vienna, Gernot Gurtler's 'Impressionen einer Reise. Das England-Itineraire des Zinzendorf 1768', *Mitteilungen des Instituts für Österreichische Geschichtsforschung* 93 (1985), pp.333–69, it is a useful introduction. More recently, Norman Scarfe has edited *A Frenchman's year in Suffolk: French impressions of Suffolk Life in 1784: including a preliminary week in London, brief visits to Cambridge, Colchester, Mistley and Harwich and a fortnight's tour of Norfolk: the Mélanges sur L'Angleterre of Francois de la Rochefoucauld, supplemented by the Journaux of Alexandre de la Rochefoucauld and the Lettres à un ami of their companion Maximilien de Lazowski* (Woodbridge, Suffolk: Boydell and Brewer, 1988); Jacques Gury has edited Marc de Bombelle's *Journal de voyage en Grande Bretagne et en Irlande, 1784* (Oxford, 1988); P. G. Hoftijzer had written 'Business and Pleasure: a Leiden bookseller in England in 1882', in Susan Roach (ed.) *Across the Narrow Seas. Studies in the history and bibliography of Britain and the Low Countries* (London, 1991), pp.178–87; and Jacques Carré had edited *Jacques Tenon, Journal d'Observations sur quelques Prisons d'Angleterre (1787)* (Clermont-Ferrand: Faculté de Lettres et Sciences humaines de L'Université Blaise-Pascal, new ser. 37, 1992). French travel literature is considered in J. Grieder, *Anglomania in France 1740–1789* (Geneva, 1985).

Travellers in Britain were particularly interested in technological progress and signs of modernity, a process that reached its apogee with the visit of Peter the Great of Russia who went to see a ship being constructed. A Newtonian world of applied science and the dramatic new utilitarian buildings of, for example, Greenwich were of interest: tourists did not tend to go to London for the sake of court or culture, ancient or modern.[4] In some respects the situation was analogous to that of modern travel today to the United States, as was the reporting of such travel.

Paris and the Mediterranean were different. Tourists visited Paris as the leading European court, and the centre of civilisation, polite society and the arts. The cultural sway of Paris developed in the seventeenth century and received tribute in, for example, the purchase of expensive furniture by German rulers, such as the Electors of Bavaria, or the introduction of the umbrella to England. Cultural images and influence also spread through publication. They might be diffused most effectively by personal impressions, and tourists, therefore, served as crucial cultural intermediaries, but the numbers involved were necessarily small. Travel

Fig.2. A Gathering of Dilettanti around the Medici Venus. By Thomas Patch. Patch lived in Florence from 1755 until his death in 1782.

literature therefore magnified the impact of tourism. The question is, how far did it also refract it?

Culture is often at the cusp between cosmopolitanism and xenophobia, between the wish to be part of, and to appreciate, the foreign, the different, the outside world; and concern and fear about just such a process, and about the apparent threats to identity and integrity that they pose. Travel and the recording of travel focus these pressures of attraction and rejection. It presents, clarifies and brings to all the sense, and, in an uncontrolled fashion, sensations and responses that had previously been controlled or limited.

This is less so in the twentieth century, because there is now greater exposure to the outside world. Foreign sights are purveyed by television and film, recipes by newspapers, foods and drinks by supermarkets. The Britons of the 1990s can buy their pasta at Sainsburys and their Chianti at Oddbins. Abroad is less foreign; indeed one of the complaints is sometimes that that is the case: that Paris has McDonalds, and Marks and Spencer. This shift is, like much else, an aspect of consumerism, technology and democratisation; the last, that large numbers can now afford to travel.

Another difference was presented by the organisation of tourism. The democratising and institutionalising of tourism that developed in the nineteenth century transformed the experience of tourism by making it a mass experience. This ensured that tourists who sought to be distinctive were reacting against other tourists as much as in response to what they were visiting. It also created a challenge for modern travel literature, most of which deliberately searches for the atypical and presents the maverick.

Thus, the eighteenth-century experience of tourism, of the foreign, the 'other', was very different from the modern one, and is difficult to put in context. It is a field in which comparisons, for example, of places visited or food consumed, can be misleading, because they fail to note the different contexts. In the modern world, food preferences have been depoliticised, and emotive issues about national identity raised by the British beef crisis of 1996 played a smaller role than those focusing on public health and regulation. In the eighteenth century food was different. Views about food were expressed within a known and understood context in which food was seen as symptomatic of moral forces and national stereotypes. Thus, all British comments on French food responded to a background belief that the French use of sauces reflected a preference for show over substance, for rich flavours over solid pieces of meat.

They was also a sense that foreigners were dishonest, and this was frequently reflected in the travel literature. Philip Thicknesse in 1768 repeatedly warned against fraud: in Paris the postillions were bribed to take tourists to particular hotels, there were sharpers, and the town was not safe for young British tourists. The Austrian Netherlands were also dangerous:

To the younger part of my countrymen who are constantly making excursions to the continent, these letters may prove useful, for I have met with none who have escaped the impositions of the lower order of the people, and but few who have been wise enough even to perceive the artifices of the upper; an order, by much the most dangerous, in general, for a young Englishman of fortune to be connected or acquainted with. I must observe therefore that strangers who are permitted to the *honour* of eating and conversing with the high and mighty people of the Pais-bas should avoid playing with them; first, because they understand play; and secondly because they do not always, as Englishmen do, pay when they lose ... Never trust to the word of a tradesman in this country, nor buy anything without paying the price and taking a receipt; there is no dependence on any man in business, nor that he will send you home the same goods you have bought.[5]

Such comments were not made humorously or in a spirit of curiosity. There was also a profound sense of unease and cultural tension on the part of the British. It is difficult to decide where to place the emphasis. It would be wrong to suggest that there was a *zeitgeist*, a spirit of the age that incorporated, refracted and influenced, if not controlled, all opinions. Far from that being the case, there were a variety of opinions. This is scarcely surprising. It is a condescension to the past to assume that past societies were less complex than those of the twentieth century. The Don Quixote approach to the past – that seventeenth-century Spanish history and culture are symbolised and summed up by the knight tilting foolishly and unsuccessfully at windmills – is misleading: which character in an Iris Murdoch novel is to be used to sum up postwar Britain?

Eighteenth-century Britain has suffered from the simplifying process, not least because of the seductive images produced by televised stories. The reification of travel is as one with this process. In fact, it was a complex society[6] and, accordingly, there were different responses to 'abroad' and to tourism. Nevertheless, it is pertinent to note that international tension – political, economic and cultural – played a role in these responses. The cultural and ideological dimension were especially important. An ideological component in Anglo-French relations preceded the French Revolution. France was seen as an autocratic Catholic state that was the reverse of Britain. This contrast was also a challenge, because France was a dynamic power, more populous and with a stronger army than Britain, and a state that expanded considerably in the seventeenth century. Furthermore, the expansion challenged Britain, as France made gains in the Low Countries, the part of the Continent seen as of most strategic interest to Britain. Finally, the French intervened in Britain from 1689 by supporting the Jacobite claimant to the throne. This challenge was an ideological, as well as a political, threat.

Thus, to visit France was to visit the national enemy. Italy was also a source of ideological challenge, although not a direct political threat. It was as if the prime destinations of American tourists at the height of the Cold War had been the Soviet Union and China. The comparison is appropriate because tourism was seen as posing a danger of seduction. Today, we tend to see the artistic seduction of eighteenth-century British tourists, their attraction to Classical sites and ambiences, to Baroque architecture and painting, to contemporary opera, and to artists such as Canaletto. Yet the seduction that posed a threat was that of Catholicism and autocracy: of the turning of the élite through travel to favour foreign ideological and political mores and precepts. The danger was not seen solely in these terms. Foreign cultural preferences could be held to be more widely indicative, to reveal political and ideological tendencies.

Fig.3. Four Learned Milordi by Joshua Reynolds, 1751. A burlesque on Raphael's *School of Athens*. Thomas, 4th Earl of Ailesbury, is on the left.

This attitude was well-established in the discussion of domestic culture, the printed polemic within Britain that was part of the context for the appearance of Grand Tour literature.[7] Criticism of British patrons of Italian opera, for example in the 1720s, and of French theatre, especially in the 1730s and 1740s, focused on their supposed role in spreading alien values. Cultural nationalism was also reflected in a positive direction, with the development of vernacular opera, ballad opera, most famously John Gay's *Beggar's Opera* (1728), and oratorio, the rediscovery of Shakespeare, and the foundation of the Royal Academy. This context for tourism was publicly expressed in press discussion about tourism.

The extent to which the tension between xenophobia and cosmopolitanism was internalised by tourists is unclear. The sources for tourist attitudes are problematic. Diaries and correspondence are not theoretical texts. They are bitty by nature, frequently allusive or elusive in comment, and do not contain explanation of background attitudes. In so far as broad trends can be discerned, it is clear that the Continent became more familiar, and thus, at the personal level, less hostile and, to a degree, de-politicised. Facilities for tourists developed, as did a structure of routes, and the tourists themselves became less alien figures.

Tourists were also affected by the growth in British cultural self-confidence that was increasingly apparent from the 1740s. The sources of this were various – the defeat of the Jacobite rising of 1745 and British victories over France and Spain in 1758–62 were especially important. The British constitution appeared clearly established, the economy was expanding, and demographic growth from the early 1740s, after a century of stagnation, was especially important. As a result, the British élite became more confident of purpose – a generalisation, but one that describes an important mid-century shift in sensibility. This greater confidence was particularly apparent in the case of British treatment of Italy. Charles Thompson in 1744 had explained his decision to visit the peninsula in terms that reflected its artistic reputation:

... being impatiently desirous of viewing a country so famous in history, which once gave laws to the world; which is at present the great school of music and painting, contains the noblest productions of statuary and architecture, and abounds with cabinets of rarities, and collections of all kinds of antiquities.

Italy, however, also became more obviously a theme-park of the past, a country de-civilised by a decadent society and culture. Italy was held to represent the past, not only the past of classical splendour and culture, the past that inspired Edward Gibbon among others, but also the past of the present. To the British, modern Italy appeared to be a land in the grip of reaction. Its reputation as a haunt of superstition and reaction became more of an issue as a consequence of the growing cult of progress, increase in change and support for tolerance that not only characterised advanced thought in Britain in this period, but was also more widely diffused in that society. Thus Italy appeared outside the process of civilisation, indeed a denial of it, as was made cruelly obvious by the classical ruins that attracted more attention during the century. This very denial attracted attention, most famously with Gibbon's masterpiece. Lady Craven was very critical of Naples, 'where the Government supplies nothing for the ease of its subjects … where public misery is concealed under national pomp'.

The British failed to appreciate the degree to which there was an Enlightenment in Italy and, more specifically, to grasp the extent to which there were attempts to reform and modernise government and society as understood by contemporary standards, particularly in Lombardy, Parma and Tuscany.

In early-seventeenth-century Britain there had been a positive response towards Italian republicanism, especially Venice, seen as a model of republican virtue, civic organisation and Catholic opposition to Habsburg hegemony and papal pretensions. By the eighteenth century, the situation was different. Venice was still seductive as a centre of culture and pleasure, but it was seen as an increasingly inconsequential state, a model only of rigidity. It was less credible than it had been to present the republican liberty and energy of classical Rome through the refracting example of Venice.[8] There was now far less interest in republicanism in Britain. Genoa's reputation was greatly damaged by the rebellions of its Corsican colony, and it too seemed inconsequential and rigid. Lucca was essentially a pleasant anomaly, a lovely backwater.

Travel to the Mediterranean meant travel to Italy. Iberia received few tourists. Spain was not regarded as the most interesting country to visit. Madrid lacked the cosmopolitan, accessible culture of Paris and its society was perceived as dull and reclusive. Outside Madrid there appeared to be little to see. There was no vogue for the beach, the mountains lacked the splendour and glamour of the Alps, the Roman antiquities were less well known than those of Italy, and there was little interest in the Moorish remains. Travelling to and in Spain also presented major difficulties. The journey there by land was very long, involved a passage across the Pyrennees and entailed poor facilities for travellers. The sea journey to Portugal was a long one, facilities outside Lisbon were poorly developed, and there was very little travel there, except for those going to Madrid, who tended to follow the main road.

Partly because so few tourists visited Iberia, it was largely known through travel literature, works such as Henry Swinburne's *Travels through Spain in the years 1775 and 1776* (1779), and Joseph Townsend's *A Journey through Spain in the years 1786 and 1787* (1791). The same was true of Sicily, with Patrick Brydone's *Tour through Sicily and Malta* (1773), Swinburne's *Travels in the Two Sicilies* (1783–5), and Brian Hill's *Observations and Remarks in a Journey through Sicily and Calabria* (1792). Thus, as more generally with travel literature, its importance was in part a product of its particular subject. Such literature did not always give an account of the most recent travel. *A Voyage to Sicily and Malta* by John Dryden, son of the poet, published in 1776, described a journey made in 1700.

There were relatively few tourists to the Balkans, Iberia, the Baltic and eastern Europe. Disease, wars and disorder affected travel to the Balkans, and hellenism and philhellenism, sympathy for Greece ancient and modern, did not become prominent until the 1790s. Fashion and convenience kept most tourists to several well-worn routes, where the whims and wishes of those who travelled for pleasure were appreciated. Across much of Europe, roads were poor and accommodation for travellers minimal. Accounts of these regions are less frequent and more adventurous, and thus tend to focus on factual details. This is true of the two most important: Nathaniel Wraxall's *Cursory Remarks made in a Tour through some of the Northern Parts of Europe* (1775) and William Coxe's *Travels into Poland, Russia, Sweden, and Denmark* (1784–90). Such works owe much to interest in current affairs. Indeed that was the theme of Coxe's preface. It referred not to interesting places but to the quality of the political sources:

... it is necessary to apprize the reader upon what foundation the principal facts are supported.

In regard to Poland, I was honoured with information from persons of the highest rank and authority; and fortunately obtained possession of some original letters written from Warsaw, before and during the Partition, which have enabled me to throw a considerable light over that interesting period. I presume, therefore, that the account of Poland comprehends many particulars, which have not been hitherto presented to the public.

With respect to Russia, as the Empress [Catherine II] herself deigned to answer some queries relative to the state of the public prisons ... The nature of the Swedish government rendered the sources of information easy to access ...[9]

Apart from negative factors of travel elsewhere, there were positive reasons for encouraging travel to France and Italy. They were fashionable countries, exciting, and fairly pleasant to visit; the hardships of travel were fewer. Such hardships were also made pleasantly predictable and readily understood by the experience of earlier travellers through the medium of print. Italy was essential to the Grand Tour, although there was no set course for travel there: preferences and circumstances varied. Tourists were influenced by the place of arrival and of expected departure; the season of the year, and the importance of avoiding the summer heat and the onset of malaria near Rome; the possible inclinations of their travelling companions; the desire to meet friends; and their wish to attend specific events; the opera in Reggio, Bologna and Milan, the Carnival in Naples and Venice, and religious, especially Easter, ceremonies in Rome.

Rome was the goal of many tourists, the furthest point of numerous tours, the reality and symbol of what was desirable about foreign travel. In a culture dominated by the classics, Rome was the focus of interest. Rome offered classical and baroque art, sculpture, architecture and painting, had the facilities a tourist could wish for, and an artistic colony that made its marvels readily accessible.

In the sixteenth century, religious schism had made Rome the seat of Antichrist, not culture, as far as Protestants were concerned, but in the seventeenth century this tension ebbed and in the eighteenth it markedly receded. Furthermore, cultural trends helped to make Rome more important. If the baroque was the culture of any place, it was the culture of Rome. It was also a culture whose impact was general to Europe and not restricted to lands under Catholic sway. The dramatic new edifices that baroque rebuilding brought to Rome, and the newly-commissioned works displayed in them, both paintings and sculpture, ensured that until the mid-eighteenth century Rome's appeal was very much that of a contemporary cultural powerhouse; the attraction of its classical past was less urgent for many tourists.

For tourists to note variety is, nevertheless, crucial. Tourism was more varied than is sometimes implied by the phrase the 'Grand Tour'. However much guided by tutors and influenced by their own expectations, and those of parents and peers, tourists were individuals seeking different objectives and following different routes. The young man aiming at a future military career who, in the late eighteenth century, attended Prussian manoeuvres in Silesia, or his counterpart who studied Alpine glaciers, had different priorities and, thus, itineraries from those who chased opera dancers in Paris or admired the contents of the Uffizi.

Given the diversity of tourist interests and experience, it is not surprising that the impact of tourism varied. There are, however, serious methodological problems in assessing first experience and then impact. There are three kinds of extant tourist writing: manuscript accounts, accounts published by contemporaries, and those published subsequently. The first and third kinds are different from the second. They were designed for personal recollection, family or friends. A lack of clarity has arisen from the habit of conflating these types of material and treating them indiscriminately as sources for the Grand Tour. Published travel literature should be differentiated from letters and journals never intended for publication, although a continuum of sorts can be observed. The preface of Patrick Brydone's *A Tour through Sicily and Malta in a series of letters to William Beckford* (1773), claimed:

Had there been any book in our language on any subject of the following Letters, they never should have seen the light. The Author wrote them for the amusement of his friends, and as an assistance to his memory; and if it will in any degree apologize for their imperfections, he can with truth declare that they never were intended for publication: nor indeed was that idea suggested to him, till long after they were written. One principal motive he will own, was the desire of giving to the world, and perhaps of transmitting to posterity, a monument of his friendship with the gentleman to whom they are addressed ... In transcribing them for the press, he found it necessary both to retrench and to amplify; by which the ease of the epistolary style has probably suffered, and some of the letters have been extended much beyond their original length.

He now presents them to the Public with the greatest diffidence; hoping that some allowance will be made for the very inconvenient circumstances, little favourable to order or precision, in which many of them were written: But he would not venture to new-model them; apprehending, that what they might gain in form and expression, they would probably lose in ease and simplicity; and well knowing that the original impressions are better described at the moment they are felt, than from the most exact recollection;[10]

the conclusion an assertion of the value of spontaneity.

Artifice could, of course, also play a part in material never intended for publication. A youth writing home to his parents might have many reasons for disguising his activities and glossing over his responses. Journals were shown to others, letters read aloud and handed around by friends and relations. Jervis wrote his journal for others to read. MacLaurin hoped that his account would be of interest to friends and relations. Perceval congratulated Edward Southwell junior on his description of Geneva and wrote of the 'pattern it gives my son how to write when it becomes his turn to voyage as you do'.

However, even if the written record was somewhat contrived, there was a difference between writing for an intimate circle and producing a work for a large anonymous market, in which the sole identifiable readers would be publishers and booksellers concerned with commercial appeal; although it is unclear how far the coverage and style established by published works affected more private accounts. The conventions expected by the market, reviewers, readers, and writers themselves definitely had to be respected in published work.

Furthermore, new works were in many senses, explicitly or, more commonly, implicitly commenting on what had gone before. In her *Observations and Reflections made in the course of a Journey through France, Italy, and Germany* (1789), Mrs Thrale/Piozzi cited Addison, Brydone, Burney, Chesterfield, Cork and Orrery, Hamilton, Howell and Moore. Borrowing was common, as indeed in many other aspects of the culture of print, such as cartography. It was not always welcome. The well-travelled John, 3rd Earl of Bute, who noted that travel writers drew heavily on other works, was unhappy with what he found in their books. He thought many of the subjects useless or improper, which he blamed on the fact that 'writing is become a trade'.[11]

Most of the well-known accounts of seventeenth- and eighteenth-century tourism fall into the category of travel literature. They vary in their methods, tone, and areas covered, but they share a concern for impact and style. It is not surprising that scholars have concentrated on these writings, some of which were by major cultural and literary figures such as Joseph Addison, who published *Letters from Italy* (1703) and *Remarks on Several Parts of Italy* (1705), which were much read by other travellers[12] and influenced the conventions of travel writing.[13]

The views expressed in travel literature are more accessible, through being printed, and the texts themselves are easier and more attractive to read then subsequently-printed accounts that were never intended for publication. In addition, many works on tourism were written by amateurs lacking the time or resources to search for manuscript sources, and by scholars of literature whose forte has generally lain elsewhere. It is not surprising that both groups have concentrated on readily accessible published material by prominent figures, without appreciating that such accounts should not be seen as necessarily typical of the writings and views of tourists, but rather as works of literature. To a certain extent, however, the modern fashion for studying discourses or 'hegemonic concepts' ensures that the coherent constructs of travel literature are actively preferred to the more bitty and amorphous responses presented in manuscript sources. It has been claimed, for example, that 'the established itinerary of statues and paintings as well as cities unified English visitors in a controlled common experience'.[14] This was true of many (although far from all) visitors, but not necessarily of their responses.

Travel literature could, and can, provide an ideological slant on what was reported and the way in which it was discussed. Writers were not neutral figures. Their works commonly sought to make specific as well as general points for a readership that did not recognise any barriers to partisan viewpoints and political images. There was no more reason why travel literature should be immune from these influences than history or religious writings, both of which were frequently heavily politicised in this period.[15] Travel literature can be seen to be removed from the experiences of ordinary tourists, not least because, in some cases, it is probable that it was written to be read as much as a form of fiction, as interesting works at times similar to picaresque novels, rather than objective descriptions of the travels of individual tourists. Travel literature provided an opportunity for autobiography and amateurism, not least in the readable context of an heroic or mock-heroic journey. Travel literature was of course not uniform, but one of the more pertinent shifts occurred in the later eighteenth century: a move from the supposedly objective to the frankly subjective.

Apparently objective travel accounts were consulted by later tourists, and cannot therefore be seen as completely distinct from the experience of the latter. Richard Lassels's *Voyage of Italy* (1670) was given as an authority 60 years later by a Catholic writer seeking to refute the notion that the Pope profited from prostitution in Rome. In 1730 Joseph Atwell cited Addison and Misson on Vesuvius. William Lee mentioned reading Addison on Venice, an anonymous tourist of 1754–5 read Thomas Nugent on Fréjus, and Addison and Misson on Florence. Thomas Brand and his charge read Addison over breakfast in Geneva in 1781. Ten years later, Richard Dreyer mentioned the recently-published *Picturesque Tour through Holland, Brabant and part of France made in 1789* (1790) by Samuel Ireland. Randle Wilbraham referred in 1793 to pursuing from Vienna 'Coxe's route by Cracow to Warsaw'.[16]

Concentrating on manuscript accounts as sources for the tourist experience is not without its problems. Much tourist correspondence is poorly catalogued and scattered in general political or family correspondence and, in consequence, difficult to find. A lot of the surviving material is anonymous, some is illegible, or provides isolated items of information concerning tourists about whom little else is known. As with the printed material, so with the unprinted; much is repetitive. Yet there is much of value, not least because of its spontaneity. Letters written on the spot and at the time are a more accurate guide to experience than the polished prose of calm recollection, however quotable or literary the latter might be. By ignoring the vast bulk of unprinted material and concentrating on a relatively small number of familiar texts, a somewhat narrow conception of tourism and of the range of responses to travel has developed.

In particular, it is necessary to understand the conventions of the genre. Writers' comments frequently suggest a sense of artificial interjection and a conscious striving after effect. This is similar to some of the paeans to nature that occurred towards the end of the century, such as John Villiers's rhapsody on the sublime vastness of the Channel and the sense of grandeur that this awakened in his soul, when the reader would rather have expected vigorous puking. There could also be a striving after a more partisan effect. In 1788 James St John offered an attack on French food:

the French peasants eat great quantities of salad; which I am inclined to think can never afford anything but an acid and unwholesome chyle; for a raw, watering vegetable, with an incongruous of oil, salt, vinegar, and spice, can never be agreeable to the nature of man; and a continued use of such a composition must be highly detrimental ... the French stew their meat to an excess that renders it sapless and dry, and very indigestible; though perhaps nature never intended that we should dress our meat at all; and therefore we hear the French continually complaining of indigestions ... The quantity of spices which the French take in their ragouts and fricassees, must be unnecessary in a temperate climate, and injure the constitution ... the French would be much superior to what they are in arts and sciences if they nourished themselves as nature intended and requires.

St John went on to suggest that a banning of soup would be in the French interest. More generally, St John contrasted British freedom and degenerate French luxury, and condemned the opulence of the Orangery at Versailles as a 'shameful' luxury when many of the poor had 'not a place to lay their heads'.

Food was the focus for much of the low-level niggling xenophobia found in some writers. Thus, Philip Thicknesse argued in 1784: 'Though the tables of all orders of people are covered with a variety of dishes, which may catch the eye, or provoke the appetite, an Englishman whose stomach is not depraved, will soon wish to see a plain wholesome dish or two of meat a la mode d'Angleterre set before him'.[17]

If there are methodological problems with assessing the tourist experience, that is even more true of attempts to evaluate the impact of tourism, although it is clear that one effect was to encourage interest in travel literature. The general impact was debated at the time, but much of the contemporary criticism was misguided, more a product of the hostility shown in some countries, especially Britain, to signs of cosmopolitan activity than of any reasoned response to the experience of travel. Tourism clearly played a significant role in encouraging the openness of the upper orders of European society to cosmopolitan influences, but this is a process that is not subject to ready assessment. There is no statistical information comparable to the measure of cosmopolitan activity offered by data on book publication: the percentage of titles published in foreign languages. As already noted, although tourist numbers clearly rose, measurement is far from easy. Of the 350 English travellers to France between 1660 and 1715 mentioned in letters, diaries and journals, only eleven acquired passes.[18]

Nevertheless, it is reasonable to speculate about the possible impact of tourism. The age-related pattern of tourism was different from that in the modern world. It was far more concentrated in the period of youth, the most formative period post-childhood, and the average tour was of greater duration than the modern counterpart. This was in part a function of the time necessarily taken up by travelling, but, more significantly, a consequence of the lesser role played by higher education and employment in the lives of the affluent young in the seventeenth and eighteenth centuries.

Because foreign tourism was principally to major cities, it also emphasised another aspect of the educational nature of travel, to use the term educational in the widest sense, as indeed it would have been understood in this period. Much of the European élite was landed in its wealth and lived in rural seats, although in some, especially Mediterranean, regions the nobility was more concentrated in the towns. Exposure to urban life did not have to wait until foreign tourism, as the landed nobility travelled to, and sometimes resided for part of the year in, cities in their own countries, but it was, nevertheless, less part of the experience of an aristocratic youth in this period than would be the case for a young tourist today. As such, as indeed more generally, the 'foreign' experience has to be understood not as a totality in which the principal measure of novelty for the tourist was that of being abroad, but as a more variable encounter in which what was different was not necessarily a product of what was foreign.

This was also true in a number of specific respects, including, most centrally, being away from a context of control. The aristocratic youth was not only away from parental supervision, but also away from the tutelary control of the educational system. The travelling tutors who accompanied many young tourists were in no position to control them: apart from anything else, many knew that their subsequent career would depend on the patronage of their young charge.

Debate over the value of the Grand Tour is the aspect of travel literature that tends to be underrated, but it was important, not least in influencing the private and public experience of travel, and the related literature. Travel accounts tended to advocate the value of travel, unsurprisingly so both as they wished to encourage readers and because many were written by 'bearleaders'. In his *New Letters from an English Traveller* (1781), Martin Sherlock claimed

Nothing is so useful as travelling to those who know how to profit by it. Nature is seen in all her shades, and in all her extremes. If the mind of the traveller be virtuous, it will be confirmed in the love of virtue, and in the abhorrence of vice; because he will everywhere see that virtue is esteemed by the persons who practise it the least. If the traveller has the seeds of one or of several talents, he will find men of the first merit in every line, who will think it a pleasure to encourage and unfold those seeds, and to communicate knowledge ... The traveller has, besides, the advantage of making continual comparisons, which strengthen his judgment extremely.[19]

Much of the debate reflected directly on this issue of lack of control and the alleged consequences in terms of heavy expenditure and personal excess; but, as already suggested, this aspect of the impact owed more to the novelty of lack of control, rather than that simply of being abroad. Thus the contemporary debate over the value of tourism was in some respects misleading, in that much of it related to a sphere – abroad – in which other pre-existing tensions or disputes, over, for example, the conduct of the young, appeal of Catholicism, or the issue of élite cultural betrayal, could be discussed. In the case of tourism these anxieties could be particularly focused, and were so with reason, as the effect of having so many of the young, who would later be influential, abroad was a sensible issue for discussion. In societies based on hereditary wealth, status and often position, the activities of heirs was a matter of acute concern; not least because, in a way, they presented the future to the present.

Yet criticism of the conduct of tourists[20] in part only served to consolidate the image of tourism as fashion. The eighteenth century was at the higher social levels increasingly a consumer society affected by fashions; news of the latter was spread by the growing number of ephemeral publications and the literature of social manners. Travel became fashionable as a means of finishing the education of youths, as a source of social polish, and as a pleasant and desirable way in which to spend periods of leisure. Cosmopolitanism[21] was redefined, away from a sense of religious identity – the strident animosities of competing camps – and towards the sense of a common European cultural inheritance.

Though religious tension remained a feature of the period, tourism to countries following a different type of Christianity ceased to be hazardous, although some inconveniences remained. Intellectual shifts played a role in this process. Eighteenth-century 'rationalism' emphasised the unity and, generally, the soundness of Christian tenets, while deriding the non-rational elements in both Catholic and Protestant observances. A stronger distinction began to be drawn between religious observance and the failings of the clergy, while, conversely, as more tourists met clerics of other churches they discovered that they were actually human and usually educated, sensible people. In addition, the power of the clergy in much of Europe was increasingly restricted and thus less of an issue. Thus, for Protestants, familiarity bred a measure of tolerance towards Catholicism when the entire Christian value system appeared to be threatened by the violence and atheism of the French Revolution.

Political preferences were largely sustained by tourism. This was certainly true of British tourists, most of whom remained convinced that Britain was the best country in Europe. Despite the hospitality they received and the access they were granted to continental society at its highest level, it would not be exaggerating to claim that many returned to Britain as better-informed xenophobes. Tourism and travel literature affirmed national identity and values, and confirmed a sense of British exceptionalism. The dedication to Sacheverell Stevens, *Miscellaneous Remarks made on the spot in a late Seven Years Tour* (a volume without a publication date, but with the dedication dated 3 July 1756) had a clear ideological agenda:

The following faithful Narrative will plainly show under what a dreadful yoke the wretched people of other nations groan, their more than Egyptian task-masters having impiously robbed them of the use of that glorious faculty, their reason, deprived them of their properties, and all this under the sacred sanction of religion

... they thus miserably lie under the scourge of the tyrant's rod and the merciless phangs of ecclesiastical power.

Most of the book was devoted to the mechanics of tourism, but it was clearly designed to have an additional purpose:

I beg leave to conclude with the following short reflection, which is, that if, from the foregoing faithful account of the wretched and miserable state of slavery and subjection, both ecclesiastical and civil, both in body and soul, other nations are reduced to by their arbitrary tyrannical governors, one single reader should be made sensible of the inestimable blessings he enjoys, be upon his guard against any attempts that may be made to deprive him of them, either by wicked ministers at home, or by enemies from abroad, and become a better subject, or a sincerer Christian and Protestant, it will afford me the highest satisfaction, and I shall flatter myself that I have not altogether laboured or lived in vain.

This contrasted markedly with the anglomania that affected large areas of Continental aristocratic and intellectual society in the second half of the century, particularly in France[22] and Germany. It is, however, difficult to present anglomania as a consequence of tourism: rather, it was the case that tourists went expecting to be impressed and accordingly were so: the values they already held received concrete validation in their impression of English society.

Comments on the political situation in other states were often related closely to reflections on social customs, a practice that responded to the utilitarian tendencies present in the loose bodies of ideas referred to as 'mercantilism', as well, subsequently, to those summarised as 'the Enlightenment'. There was a strong interest in such matters as poor relief and the punishment of criminals. The situation in the Dutch cities was of particular interest to tourists in the seventeenth century, as the Dutch seemed more advanced in the effective institutionalisation of care and control. This remained a topic of interest in the following century. Visiting Amsterdam in 1708, the young Lord Charles Somerset praised the 'Rasphouse' where 'fellows that are above measure idle and debauched were forced to work'. He reflected, 'If we had this excellent way of managing idle vagabonds at their first beginning in wickedness, we should save ourselves frequently from losing our money and now and then our lives with it, and those miserable wretches from losing theirs on the Gallows, and with it a great venture of their after being'.[23] Having visited the workhouse in Lille in 1764, Thomas Greene observed that the British should adopt the regulation that the 'overseers set out so much work as would be a pretty good days work and for their encouragement all that they do more they are paid for'.[24] Lady Craven praised the caution shown in dispensing drugs in Venice: 'You cannot buy a drug at the apothecaries here, without an order from a physician. A very prudent caution against the madness of those who choose to finish their existence with a dose of laudanum, or their neighbours with one of arsenic'.[25]

There were also comments on economic activity. Thus the American Quaker, Jabez Maud Fisher, who travelled in Britain in the 1770s, was interested in many matters that had no direct bearing on his business interests. He visited the Dolcoath mine in Cornwall and found, 'The Grotto lighted with a vast Number of Candles carelessly stuck with Clay to the Sides ... Fountains of Water spouting in many places and running in wild Meanders to the Bottom of the Engines where the Noise of the Pumps made the hollow Cavern resound with Echo ... the Place was too terrible to be viewed without Fright and Astonishment'. The visual impact of industrial change was another theme. At Coalbrookdale, Fisher stayed with a fellow-Quaker, Abraham Darby III, and recorded both a detailed account of the ironworks and a more emotional response: 'all the horrors that Pandemonium could show ... an immense Theatre, lighted only by the Streams of Light which rise from the Furnaces ... the Craters of the burning Mountains'.[26]

In travel literature it was more common to accompany such remarks with political reflections, as in the discussion of French roads in an anonymous *Tour of Holland* (1772): 'The roads are excellent, and untaxed with turnpikes; but these the poor peasants are obliged to make and to repair by the sweat of their brow, without even the prospect of advantage accruing to them from their labour'.[27]

Yet, it would be misleading to suggest that most tourists or travel writers made no economic commentary. But what was noted was generally unsystematic: references to a particularly notable or spectacular establishment, such as the Gobelins tapestry works in Paris, the nearby Sèvres porcelain factory, and the famous cloth factory set up at Abbeville in 1675 by the Dutchman Van Robais. One anonymous British tourist noted of the last 'in some of the apartments you see the looms which weave the cloth, in others the people who card the wool, in another part the dye house and in short everything laid out with the utmost convenience'.[28] The method of ploughing and other basic agricultural information also often aroused comment. However, this was far from the commentaries of Arthur Young on French agriculture[29] or Count Karl von Zinzendorf on British industry and mining. Such writers concentrated on the economy and sought to be comprehensive and systematic, but this was far from the intention of most tourists.

In general, tourists devoted more attention to the arts than the economies of the countries they visited. Acquiring knowledge of the arts was a reason advanced to justify tourism, and, judging from surviving letters and journals, many tourists were not uncritical purchasers and praisers of foreign art. The length of foreign tours, the guidance available, both from experienced tutors and from local guides, and the interest of most tourists, helped to ensure that many acquired considerable experience in assessing operas, paintings and buildings. Some were more critical than others, but standards were high, in general, and tourism served to enrich the élite culturally.

Artistic criticism can of course be just as frequently a sign of ignorance or prejudice as of discernment; political and religious biases could colour responses. And yet, it is striking how far tourists sought to counter such prejudices and to respond to paintings as works of art. A lively interest in architecture was one of the attributes of gentility and many members of the élite were knowledgeable enough to play a role in the construction or alteration of stately houses. Tastes varied, but were clearly affected by printed art criticism. There was a marked preference for the Classical over the Gothic that led most tourists to slight medieval buildings and to ignore or dislike the architecture of Germany, most of provincial France, and some of northern Italy. Old towns and quarters were disliked; the preference was for wide, straight streets, as in Turin or the newer sections of Marseilles. George Berkeley praised the regularity of Catania, rebuilt in Baroque style after the devastating earthquake of 1693.[30] Narrow, twisting streets were associated with dirt, disease and poverty. Many of the buildings that tourists admired were relatively modern, Classical or Baroque in style – St Paul's in London, the Invalides in Paris, palaces such as Versailles and the Upper and Lower Belvederes in Vienna. An emphasis on novelty ensured that the new ideas and images disseminated in print were of particular interest, but so also did a focus on a past that was mediated through print, the Classical past.

The strong influence of a Classical education and of a public ideology that drew strongly on Classical images and themes can be seen in the accounts of many tourists. The Italian Classical remains and sites that most tourists saw were Roman. The large number of sites near Naples was the furthest south that most travelled, though many went from Naples to Paestum on the Gulf of Salerno. The Greek temples there played a major role in the controversy of the late 1760s over the respective merits of Greek and Roman styles. It was only a small number of tourists, and those mostly later in the century, who visited the Greek sites in Sicily. The discovery of Pompeii and Gavin Hamilton's excavations around Rome (1769–92) stimulated great interest in sculpture and the seeds of full-blown Neo-Classicism, as against the earlier Greek v. Roman debate, were sown by this interest.

Yet there were also different views. In 1770 John, 3rd Earl of Bute, formerly the favourite and leading minister of George III, and, after his resignation, a cultured and well-travelled connoisseur, wrote,

> ... had it pleased Providence to destroy the works, the writings, the very memory of the Greeks and Romans with their Empires, we now should brag of poets, architects, sculptors, etc. as we do of Newtons, Raphaels and other superior beings, whose vast inventive geniuses have soared to science and arts, that scarce were known before, Milton would have wrote a divine poem, though he had never known Homer; [Robert] Adam would have erected buildings worthy of the British nation, in a British taste, and instead of wandering to Spalato [Split] for the remains of Diocletian's palace.[31]

Bute captured one of the central features of culture, and thus leisure, in the seventeenth and eighteenth centuries: the emphasis on the past. This was true more generally of the period. It was reverential of and referential to the past, and in that, as in so much else, the 'early-modern period' can be seen as a continuation of the Middle Ages. Aspects of novelty – gunpowder, printing, the creation of transoceanic empires, the Reformation schism in Western Christendom – were subsumed in a system the basic lineaments of which were very conservative: low productivity agriculture as the basis of the economy, limited energy sources, an absence of rapid and easy transportation, inegalitarianism in wealth and opportunity, the dominance of birth, status and privilege, the subordination of women, respect for age, limited literacy and education.

The Grand Tour was a reflection of this society, but so, more particularly, was the emphasis on the past that characterised much tourism. As already indicated, there was a different set of priorities focusing on interest in social institutions, economic progress and technological developments, but these were minority concerns, as indeed they would always be in the history of tourism: travelling for economic advantage is not at issue here, as commentators, such as Young, were primarily motivated by interest and were not being paid.

Any theme of cultural clash in the field of tourism has to be handled with caution. Tourists from Britain, the great economic powerhouse in the eighteenth and nineteenth centuries, wished to visit the Classical sites of Europe, and, in the nineteenth century, added the Alps and the shores of the Mediterranean: they were not in search of industrial plant along the Meuse or Ruhr, any more than modern Japanese tourists. Furthermore, the mechanics of travel was of greater interest. It played a major role in travel literature. Thus, for example, in his *Miscellaneous Remarks made on the spot in a late Seven Years Tour* (no date), Sacheverell Stevens described a journey from Marseilles to Genoa in 1739 in part in order to advise future tourists:

On Sunday, May 31, I embarked in a felucca for Italy, having first laid in a good stock of provision, as cold tongues, ham, bread, wine etc. This precaution will be of service to those who may perform this voyage; for in these feluccas it is uncertain where you may be drove to, which was my case; for we had not sailed above a day and a half, when the weather began to be extremely bad, and the sea became so rough and boisterous, that the waves very near beat over us; the mariners were now terribly daunted, the boat being half full of water; and for want of pails, etc. to fling it out, we were obliged to make use of our hats ... I grew so sick that I could do no service.[32]

Storms at sea reflected another dimension of travel not true of all of the genre, but adventure was integral to many travelogues, especially if experience with the unfamiliar can be seen in that light. At times the adventure was more explicit. Joseph Shaw became lost on the road from Amersford to Dieren:

... on the fine heath ... about nine of the clock, after having been for some hours alone in the endless desert, not able to speak one word of the language of the country, we found the road split into two; and absolute darkness had now rendered our eyes of so little use, that we were all forced to alight, and for about half an hour with our hands grope, and by the largeness of the tracks to discover the most probable way. In this condition we were reduced to such a perplexed uncertainty, that the Doctor was for taking up his quarters there all night, and I had much ado (though backed both by the coachman and footman) to persuade him to pursue that way that seem'd probable, and which, how probable soever it seemed, in about an hour grew so very narrow, as to admit one coach abreast, and brought us at last into a wood, so thick, that the trees hindered us from advancing any faster than an insensible pace, and gave me some slight apprehensions of mischief; augmented by the Doctor's representations of our wickedness in travelling on the Sabbath and of the probability of a conspiracy between the coachman and footman in their language ... to decoy us into a place so horrid on some bloody design ... on a sudden, in the middle of this dark wood, some men cried out aloud Hold – stand! ... I thought I heard the signal for an attack that would probably put an end to my travels with my life, and immediately cocked my pistols.

Happily for Shaw the mysterious callers were other travellers.[33]

Bute grasped another contrast that is also pertinent today: that between tourism focused on the appreciation of the past and an interest in travel for pleasure that was reverential of the past. In the eighteenth century it was still the case that the past prevailed, but there were already signs of a shift in sensibility, interest and itineraries. By the 1780s William Beckford was already enthusing about wild, primitive scenery, while in 1786 Joseph Townsend rode on horseback from Leon to Oviedo, 'through the wildest and most romantic country which can be imagined, rendered tremendous by the rocks and beautiful by the wood and water'.[34] There was greater interest in wilder scenery and sensations. Switzerland became a goal, rather than an obstacle. It was no longer necessary for a mountain, waterfall or lake to have been mentioned by Virgil or Livy for it to attract tourists.

The Romantic sensibility marked the end of the conventional Grand Tour, although not as clearly as the French Revolution was to do. When tourists began to visit Italy again in large numbers from 1815 on, their mental world was different from that of their predecessors. It would be misleading to exaggerate change, but after 1815 the past was being looked at from the perspective of a present that increasingly was less shaped by the impact of earlier centuries.

References

1.   On the Grand Tour see, in particular, J. Black, *The British and the Grand Tour* (London, 1985) and J. Black, *The British Abroad. The Grand Tour in the Eighteenth Century* (Stroud, 1992).

2.   Andrews, *Letters to a Young Gentleman* (London, 1784), pp.477–8. On travel literature, Black, 'Tourism and Cultural Challenge: The Changing Scene of the Eighteenth Century', in J. McVeagh (ed.), *English Literature and the Wider World. Volume I 1660–1780. All Before Them* (London, 1990), M. Cohen, 'The Grand Tour: Constructing the English Gentleman in Eighteenth-Century France', *History of Education*, 21 (1992).

3.   On the earlier situation see, in particular, J. Stoye, *English Travellers Abroad, 1604–1667* (New Haven, 1989); E. Chaney, *The Grand Tour and the Great Rebellion: Richard Lassells and 'The Voyage of Italy'* (Geneva, 1985).

4.   R. Porter, 'Visitors' Visions: Travellers' Tales of Georgian London', in C. Chard and H. Langdon (eds), *Transports: Travel, Pleasure, and Imaginative Geography, 1600–1830* (New Haven, 1996), pp.31–47.

5.   P. Thicknesse, *Useful Hints to those who make the Tour of France* (London, 1768), pp.134–5, 160–2, *A Year's Journey through the Pais Bas and Austrian Netherlands*

(London, 1784), pp.3–4, 49, 6; J. Black, 'A Stereotyped Response? The Grand Tour and Continental Cuisine', *Durham University Journal*, 83 (1991).

6. As is stressed in J. Black, *An Illustrated History of Eighteenth-Century Britain* (Manchester, 1996).

7. H. J. Müllenbrock, 'The political implications of the Grand Tour: Aspects of a specifically English contribution to the European travel literature of the age of Enlightenment', *Trema*, 9 (1984).

8. C. Thompson, *The Travels of the late Charles Thompson* (3 vols, Reading, 1744), I, 67; Craven, *Memoirs of the Margravine of Anspach* (2 vols, London, 1826) I, 306–7; B. Redford, *Venice and the Grand Tour* (New Haven, 1996).

9. W. Coxe, *Travels into Poland, Russia, Sweden and Denmark* (3rd edn, 4 vols, 1787) I, ix–x.

10. P. Brydone, *Tour through Sicily and Malta* (2nd edn, London, 1774) I, v–vii.

11. Bute to John Symonds, from 1771 Professor of Modern History at Cambridge, 1770, Cambridge University Library, Additional Manuscripts vol.8826.

12. P. Smiths, *The Life of Joseph Addison* (2nd edn, Oxford, 1968), p.105.

13. C. L. Batten, *Pleasurable Instruction* (Berkeley, 1978).

14. P. M. Spacks, 'Splendid Falsehoods: English Accounts of Rome, 1760–1798', *Prose Studies*, 3 (1980), p.206.

15. J. Black, 'Ideology, history, xenophobia and the world of print in eighteenth-century England', in J. Black and J. Gregory (eds), *Culture, Politics and Society in Britain 1660–1800* (Manchester, 1991).

16. New Haven, Beinecke Library, Osborn Shelves c 266 1, p.95; Atwell to Lady Sarah Cowper, 13 May 1730, Hertford, County Record Office, D/EP F 234; Beinecke, Lee papers Box 3, 26 Ap. 1753, Osborn Shelves c 200 pp.68, 99, f.c. 11 p.43, Osborn Files 33, 159; London, British Library, Additional Manuscripts 5831 f.7; Brand to his sister Susan, 16 Jan., Cambridge University Library, Additional Manuscripts 8670/10; Chester, County Record Office, DBW/N/Bundle 4 no.4.

17. [Villiers], *A Tour through part of France* (London, 1789), p.7; J. St John, *Letters from France to a Gentleman in the South of Ireland written in 1787* (Dublin, 1788), pp.75–7, 81, 127–8, 95, 36–7; Thicknesse, *A Year's Journey through the Pais Bas and Austrian Netherlands*, p.177.

18. David Sturdy, 'English Travellers in France 1660–1715' (unpublished PhD. thesis, Dublin, 1969), pp.78–9.

19. M. Sherlock, *New Letters from an English Traveller* (London, 1781), pp.147–9.

20. J. Black, *The British Abroad. The Grand Tour in the Eighteenth Century* (Stroud, 1992), pp.297–300.

21. J. Black, *Europe in the Eighteenth Century* (2nd edn, London, 1999), pp.292–8.

22. J. Grieder, *Anglomania in France 1740–1789* (Geneva, 1985). The most recent work on tourism in the United Provinces is C. D. Van Strien, *British Travellers in Holland during the Stuart Period. Edward Browne and John Locke as Tourists in the United Provinces* (Leiden, 1993). The bibliography is a valuable guide to earlier work.

23. Badminton House, Somerset, Beaufort papers, Lord Charles Somerset, 'An account of my Travels', pp.14–15.

24. Preston, Lancashire County Record Office, DD Gr F/3, f.12.

25. Elizabeth, Lady Craven, *A Journey through the Crimea to Constantinople* (Dublin, 1789), I, 151–2.

26. *An American Quaker in the British Isles. The Travel Journals of Jabez Maud Fisher, 1775–1779*, ed. by K. Morgan (Oxford, 1992), pp.107–8, 264.

27. Anon., *Tour of Holland* (London, 1772), p.230.

28. New Haven, Beinecke Library, Osborn Files, 3.422.

29. A. Young, *Travels during the Years 1787, 1788 and 1789* (2nd edn, London 1794).

30. Chaney, 'Architectural Taste and the Grand Tour: George Berkeley's Evolving Canon', *Journal of Anglo-Italian Studies*, 1 (1991), pp.74–91, 87.

31. Bute to Symonds, 1770, Cambridge University Library, Additional Manuscripts, 886926.

32. Stevens, *Miscellaneous Remarks*, pp.82–91.

33. J. Shaw, *Letters to a Nobleman* (London, 1709), pp.7–9.

34. Liston papers, Edinburgh, National Library of Scotland, vol. 545, f.9.

The English-language guide book to Europe up to 1870

GILES BARBER

THE IMPACT OF AIR TRAVEL since World War II has been such that a large part of the population of Britain, both young and old, have now travelled abroad and the latter word now stands not just for Europe but for almost any part of the world. The aim of this paper is more historical and to trace, not so much the world of the Renaissance to nineteenth-century explorer but the growing fashion during those centuries for more personal tours and holidays, the latter perhaps a different and later concept, on continental Europe and to track the evolution of the English-language guide book to serve this market, together with the manner in which the booktrade has served it.

The English are fond of extolling their love of travel and the bibliographer approaching the subject starts with a very solid base. Watt's *Bibliotheca Britannica* is, as ever, most useful, its 'journeys, tours, etc' heading always making an excellent starting point.[1] Then the wonderfully solid work of that eccentric American Fellow of Magdalen College, Oxford, W. A. B. Coolidge, charts the important Swiss field in the detailed and methodical way which was perhaps taught him by his accompanying aunt and dog, the latter of whom received an additional medal for each of the Alpine passes he reached.[2] Sir George Fordham's work on early French itineraries, C. P. Brand's and later R. S. Pine-Coffin's bibliographies on British and American travel to Italy, Pollak and Schudt's *Le Guide di Roma*, and the admirable articles of both the late de Beers, Esmond and Sir Gavin, have been a first rate starting point from which to work.[3] Of recent years there have also been a flood of books of all sorts on the Grand Tour, one of the latest being Jeremy Black's very informed *The British abroad: the Grand Tour in the eighteenth century* (1992), not forgetting the various bibliographies of Murray's and Baedeker's guides.[4] To which one must today of course also add that universal modern source, the catalogues available through the World Wide Web, and, at the risk of appearing old-fashioned, another to which I would particularly like to pay tribute since it has, throughout my lifetime in research, been one of the most important: booksellers' catalogues. The knowledge of, and the location of, material is one thing but the personal and often very learned presentation of books – not to mention the possibility of acquiring them – is another and I would here like to pay my own very grateful tribute to the numerous antiquarian booksellers who have, to my intellectual if not always financial, profit, listed, described, quoted from, and discussed so many guide books – and other items, over the years.

One should start by fixing certain boundaries and definitions. We are concerned here with the mainland of continental Europe. Equally I have given myself a terminus at 1870 because by then the railway system is well established while bicycle, car and air travel are still some way in the future; the Franco-Prussian War (like many wars) engendered a new series of 'post war' guides; the first American-based guide came about then – not to mention the first more detailed 'Guide to Paris by night'! *The Oxford English Dictionary* quotes the word 'guide' as meaning a book from 1759, and 'guidebook' as existing from 1823, while 'handbook' dates from 1836. Earlier relevant terms include 'grand tour' from 1670, 'tourist' from 1800 and 'tourism' from 1811. Other earlier works in this field used titles such as 'Description', 'Voyage' or 'Journey', 'View' or 'Picture' and I shall include some in my remarks but the sort of work I am concerned with is essentially one of those William Carr refers to in 1691 when he opposes Sir William Temple's famous *Observations on the Netherlands*, a work to be read at home in one's study, with his own book, for 'travellers ... for whose information this small essay is designed', that is with a, usually pocket size, work which the traveller is expected to take with him and to consult on the spot.[5] Constitutional, historical, artistic and other travel literature exists, as do countless personal accounts or letters, many of which claim on the title-page to be intended to assist travellers, but on the whole I have left these out (barring certain early ones on a digressive principle) so as to keep more of an eye on the evolution of the market for the 'vade mecum' type of book.

This approach owes much to Esmond de Beer and his fundamental article in the *Journal of the British archaeological association* in 1952.[6] De Beer defines the guide under three points: first, it is impersonal, systematic and with one overriding purpose; second, it combines inventory and itinerary; thirdly, it is portable and practical, for use on the spot. Guides can be said to date back to Classical antiquity if we include Pausanias's Greece while others such as the *Itineraria* of Antoninus Augustus (*c*.300 AD), covering the whole of the Roman empire, certainly give lists of places along roads to various centres, distances in post stages, and aim at major attractions such as Rome or Compostella. Rome attracted pilgrims from at least the ninth century and by the twelfth there are lists of the monuments there, together with their legends, the *Mirabilia*, while by the fourteenth and fifteenth one finds the *Indulgentiae* with their record of the churches, relics and associated indulgencies. By the sixteenth century the literature has become more humanistic, with Palladio compiling a general account of the buildings, but in the present context one should note that the 1557 *Le cose maravigliose dell'alma città di Roma* contains 'un breve Trattato delle Antichità, chiamato La Guida Romana' and ascribed to a mysterious writer called 'Schakerlay inglese'.[7] The first really modern guide was however Pompilio Totti's *Ritratto di Roma moderna* (1638), a secular guide for tourists, dealing with monuments and works of art, and covering the city region by region. This was closely followed by Fioravante Martinelli's *Roma ricercata* (1645), the novelty of which was to divide the city into ten daily walks based on the cheap tourist hotel, l'Albergo dell'Orso. This was translated in 1654 by Henry Cogan as *The Court of Rome and directions for such as shall travel to Rome, how they may view all the rarities* etc. In general therefore most major Italian towns had their guide by 1660, other capital cities such as Amsterdam, Paris and London being covered in the next 40 years. Guides to whole countries came a fraction later, starting just before 1600 with François Schott's *Itinerarium Italiae*. This work had strange origins in that a German prince visiting Italy in 1574/75 and dying in Rome, his life was written in 1587 by S. V. Pighius. Schott adapted this account for his nephew, leaving out all personal matters, transposing everything to the second person and amplifying the account of Rome from other sources. Later revisions and translations by Italians greatly improved the book and editions of it continued to come out up to 1761 – although the prince's original route remained unvaried until 1731! To round off this introductory survey one can note that up to 1725 or so guides tend to follow a single round or circular route, the technique of working from a number of centralised starting points – say Rome, Venice, Hamburg – coming in from around 1700. However by 1787 the *Vera guida d'Italia* used 31 routes from 11 different centres, this approach being later the standard pattern for Murray, Baedeker etc.

Coming to the strictly English-language guide, one should doff one's cap to two early works: the anonymous *Information for pilgrims unto the Holy Land* [London, Wynkyn de Worde, 1498, later editions 1515, 1524, and E. G. Duff's, 1893], an itinerary with notes on money; and Andrew

Boorde's *First book of the introduction of knowledge* (1542). This was edited for the Early English Text Society by F. J. Furnivall in 1870, the editor being so strongly francophobe that his preface includes the following outburst: 'And now comes the angry roar of war to trouble one's sweet content, to make one feel it wrong almost to think of private pleasures or society's work. What interest can one take in printers' dates, or Boorde's allusions, when the furious waves of French vainglory, driven by the guilty ambition of a consciousless adventurer, are dashing against the barriors of German patriotism, striving to deluge thousands of innocent homes in blood? May this Napoleon and his followers be humbled into the dust!'.[8] Boorde is perhaps more of a geography book, covering England, Scotland, Wales, Ireland, the Low Countries, Germany, Poland, Hungary, Greece, Italy, France, Spain, Turkey and Egypt, and describing the form of government, the people, and some buildings, while also giving certain useful phrases.

Thirty five years later, in 1576, came *The post for divers parts of the world*: 'to travail from one notable citie unto an other, with a description of the antiquitie of divers famous cities in Europe. Very necessary and profitable for Gentlemen, merchants, factors, or any other persons disposed to travail. The like not heretofore in English'. Published by, and therefore recorded by STC under, Richard Rowlands (STC 21360), it was 'imprinted at London by T. East', and was in 12°. Rowlands (*fl.*1565–1620), studied at Christ Church, Oxford, before moving to Antwerp around 1580 and setting up there as a printer. There he took his grandfather's name of Verstegan and became well known for his highly illustrated *Theatrum crudelitatum* (1580), a work of Catholic martyrology covering the executions of Fisher, More and Mary Stuart. He later moved to Paris and then Seville. The present work, dedicated to Sir Thomas Gresham, is 'for such gentlemen as are addicted to travail' and apparently translated 'from Almaine', although it seems rather to come from Cherubino di Stella's *Poste per diverse parti del mondo*, first published in Lyons four years earlier, in 1572. Another itinerary with brief descriptions, it covers Germany, Austria, Poland, Switzerland, Italy, England and Spain.

With the advent of the seventeenth century the pace of travel and of interest in it quickens notably: in 1604 Sir Richard Dallington's *The view of France* is accompanied by a twelve-page supplement *A method of travel*, which lists what should be observed and gives hints on dress, money and the like. An anonymous 'A true description and direction of what is most worthy to be seen in all Italy' (shortly after 1610) seems to survive only in its reprinted form in the *Harleian Miscellany* (vol.5, 1745) but only just precedes such notable travel books as Thomas Coryate's *Coryate's crudities hastily gobbled up in six months travel* (1611) and Fynes Moryson's *An itinerary* of 1617. James Howell's general advice book, *Instructions for foreign travel* (1642), sets the tone for the period while John Raymond's *An itinerary*, containing a voyage made through Italy in the year 1646 (published 1648), while detailed and early, is really more of a personal account.

The Grand Tour is however beginning to get under way and 1660 sees Edmund Warcupp's translation of Schott's *Itinerarium Italiae*, a work of which there were 18 seventeenth-century editions, which appeared under the title *Italy in all its original glory, ruin and revival: being an exact survey of the whole geography and history of that famous country ... and whatever is remarkable in Rome (the Mistress of the World)*. The first really popular English guide book was nevertheless Richard Lassels's *The Voyage of Italy; or, a compleat journey through Italy. With the characters of the people, and the description of the chief towns, churches, monasteries, tombs, libraries, pallaces, villas, gardens, pictures, statues and antiquities. As also of the interest, government, riches, forces, etc of all the princes, with instructions concerning travel*. This influential posthumous work by an Oxford man who had been five times to Italy between 1635 and 1665 as governor to various young men, turned catholic priest and become professor of classics at Douai, was edited by a friend and first published in Paris in 1670. It was reprinted at London in the same year and then further reprinted in 1685, 1686, 1698 and 1705, with French and German translations coming out in 1671 and 1673. The runner-up to Lassels was the English translation (all this underlining the already very international nature of the guide book market) of François Misson's *Nouveau voyage d'Italie* (1691), the *A new voyage to Italy* (1695), with reprints that year and in 1699, not to mention later ones. Other more specialised books or works on other towns were also begining to come out. William Lodge's translation of Giacomo Barri's book of 1671, *The painter's voyage of Italy,* appeared in 1679 introducing Guercino, Guido Reni and the Carracci to the English, while Leti's Geneva came out in 1681, Morellet's Versailles in 1684, and Germain Brice's standard work, the *New description of Paris,* in 1687.

Holland and the Netherlands were clearly crucial countries in these years and the work by the sometime consul at Amsterdam (the sort of post which often led to such authorship) Sir William Carr, *An accurate description of the United Netherlands*, 1691, contained in later editions (1730 plus) an important supplement giving *Some necessary directions whereby one may see at what time the passage-boats and waggons go off in Holland, Friesland and Germany: collected for the use and benefit of travellers*, all this evidently betokening a ready and regular transport system. By 1731 the *Guide for English travellers through Holland* was available from its Rotterdam publisher, Thomas Johnson, presumably an English bookseller established there and, like others, using his local knowledge and English to exploit a profitable passing trade.

As we have seen, a number of guide books contained a selection of useful phrases in foreign languages and this section developed during the eighteenth century into a small separate genre of its own. Some of these are however also illuminating as to the cultural level and general purposes of travellers. Jonathan Richardson's *An account of some of the statues, bas-reliefs, drawings and pictures in Italy* (1722) says in its preface: 'Whoever would Travel with Advantage ought to have the Languages, a competant Stock of Learning, and other Gentleman-like Accomplishments, Civility, Good Nature, Prudence, and a Becoming, and Insinuating Manner, to which Personal Agreeableness does not a little contribute. And before he sets out he ought to know as much of what he goes chiefly to Observe upon, as can be learn'd at home: Add to all this a hearty Love for that particular Study; and proper Recommendations. Thus he will not only Judge Better, and more Readily, of what he sees, but get easier Admission, and have greater Opportunities of seeing'.[9] One can contrast this high level approach with the specimen French/German/Italian conversation with the chambermaid given in *The Gentleman's Pocket Companion for travelling into Foreign Parts* published in the same year (1722):[10]

'God keep you from misfortune, my Host!'
'You are welcome, Gentlemen!'
   'Shall we be well lodged with you for this night?'
'Yes, very well, Sir'
   'Have you good stable, good hay, good oats, good litter, good wine?'
'The best, Sir'.   [Then after dinner where he drinks too much]:
   'By your leaves, gentlemen, I find myself somewhat indisposed'
'Sir, if you are not well, go take your rest. Your chamber is ready. Joan (the chambermaid), make a good fire in his room, and let him want for nothing'
   'Sweetheart, is my bed made? Is it good, clean, warm?'
'Yes, Sir, it is a good feather bed. The sheets are very clean'
   'Pull off my stockings, and warm my bed, for I am much out of order. I shake like a leaf in a tree. Warm a napkin for my head and bind it well. Gently, you bind it too hard. Bring my pillow and cover me well; draw the curtains and pin them together. Where is the chamber-pot? Where is the privy?'

'Follow me and I will show you the way. Go straight up and you will find it on your right hand; if you see it not you will soon smell it. Sir, do you want anything else?'

'Yes, my dear, put out the candle and come nearer to me'

'I will put it out when I am out of the room; What is your will? Are you not well enough yet?'

'My head lies too low, raise up the bolster a little. I cannot lie so low. My dear, give me a kiss, I should sleep better'

'You are not sick since you talk of kissing. I would rather die than kiss a man in his bed, or any other place. Take your rest in God's name. God give you a good night and a good rest'

'I thank you fair maid!'.

And all this forty years before Sterne, the lady he has to share with, and the 'Fille de Chambre'!

The majority of guides were what the late Howard Nixon used to call certain bindings – 'oncers' – and few ran to later editions; they were too probably the only publication of that kind put out by that particular publisher. As the number of travellers increased – a remarkable thing in view of the wars raging across Europe during the eighteenth century – so did the market for guides, and, slowly, publishers began to specialise in this field. The first major item of this kind was the anonymous *The Gentleman's guide in his tour through France. Wrote by an officer in the Royal Navy, who lately travelled on a principle which he most sincerely recommends to his countrymen, viz. Not to spend more money in the country of our natural enemy, than is requisite to support, with Decency, the character of an English Man* (1766). This book is one of the few in the eighteenth century, for which it is actually worth consulting the Stationers' Hall copyright register since that work, so useful for earlier centuries, turns up trumps on this occasion too and gives one, under 13 June, the name of the author: Philip Playstowe.[11] Not that we learn much even then but it is satisfactory to have a name and therefore to be able to add that Playstowe was gazetted as a naval lieutenant in 1757 (and may therefore have been born about 1740), was on convalescent leave in 1763 when he visited at least Brussels and Aix, and died just before 1783.[12]

The first edition of *The Gentleman's Guide* is an octavo of 124 pages and was published at Bristol (possibly Playstowe's home port) by the Quaker, Samuel Farley the Third, sometime the proprietor of *Farley's Bath Journal*. The title-page records however that it was also sold, in London, by Thomas Cadell, Mrs Palmer, A. Brown, A. Millar, and G. Kearsley, and in Oxford by Mr Fletcher, in Cambridge by Fletcher and

Hodson, and in Dublin by Smith and son. It gives the various ways of travelling from London to Paris, a description of Paris and its principal 'curiosities', public entertainments and their different prices, before going on to rules for an Englishman's laying out his money. There are also lists of Paris hotels, restaurants, language masters, fencing and dancing masters. The *Gentleman's Guide* then continues with Versailles and other nearby châteaux, and routes to Lyons, Marseilles, Toulouse and Bordeaux.

Playstowe's *Guide*, which never actually bore his name, was an immediate success, there being editions in 1767, 1768, 1770, and on up to the tenth in 1788. It was taken over at once by the London bookseller George Kearsley (the arrested publisher of Wilkes's *North Briton*), constantly expanded, and reached 360 pages by the time of the French Revolution, although one can note that the format changed to a more pocketable duodecimo from the fourth edition on. Later editions included hotels in other towns, such as Tours, and added the names of the cafés (Conti, Dauphin, Procope) frequented by the English and where London newspapers could be read – perhaps an early pointer to English gregariousness abroad.

Playstowe's *Guide* is the exact contemporary of Smollett's *Travels through France and Italy* (1766) and of Sterne's *Sentimental journey* (1768). Sound statistical evidence on the numbers of English persons abroad is however hard to come by: anecdotal evidence mentions 50 in Rome at any one time in 1692; 50 are equally said to be regularly in Lyons in transit in 1739, while in 1785 Gibbon suggests that there are 40,000 on the continent. Four hundred English families are reported to be in Naples in 1817 and the following year it is reported that 90,000 have left the country for Europe in the two preceding years.[13] Foreign travel clearly took an upsurge after the Seven Years' War (1756–63), some travellers not being 'Grand Tourists' but more like day or very short range trippers. The 1770s and 1780s reflected these trends in satirical works such as Samuel Foote's comedy *A trip to Calais* (1778), possibly based on Hogarth's 'The Calais gate', and the 1784 pantomime 'The Picture of Paris'. Kearsley saw the opening in the market and published Harry Peckham's *Tour of Holland* in 1772, the *Sketch of a tour through Swisserland* by Thomas Martyn, the professor of botany at Cambridge, in 1787, and the latter's *Gentleman's guide in his tour through Italy* in 1787. The preface to the 1791 edition of the latter archly asks itself why is there need for yet another book on Italy, replying that most are written 'to be read by the fireside at home, rather than to accompany a man abroad; to amuse the indolent, rather than to instruct the active' and claims to be 'not so much an entertaining friend to converse with at home, as a useful companion for the pocket abroad'. All of these thus not only went through several editions before the turn of the century but survived the enormous hiatus in easy (but in fact not quite all) foreign travel caused by the Revolutionary and Napoleonic wars, the 25 years where, apart from the brief and ill-fated interval of the Peace of Amiens, English people saw themselves largely confined to the beauties of the lakes, Wales and Scotland. The result was of course that after Waterloo in particular the flood gates opened, immediately somewhat surprising the publishing trade who therefore rushed out minimally updated versions of their old guide books. One of the most surprising of these was Cornelius Cayley's *A tour through Holland, Flanders and part of France* (1815), a reprint of texts originally published, some 40 years earlier, in the *Leeds Weekly Newspaper* around 1775. Playstowe and Martyn's guides also resurface, claiming to be new works by a pseudonymous H. Coxe, and now published by a new specialist firm, Sherwood, Neely and Jones, who probably moved into this market after Kearsley's came to an end in 1813.

The most successful new general book was one of the first guides by a woman: Mariana Starke's *Information and directions for travellers on the Continent* (1820), also termed just *Travels on the Continent*. Miss Starke, or 'Jack Starke' as she was commonly called, from her fancy of wearing as her ordinary dress a tall hat and a riding habit, was principally concerned with Italy however, where she had been as early as 1792, her letters of that date already containing 'Instructions for the use of Invalids and Families who may not choose to incur the Expence attendant upon travelling with a courier', a foretaste of her personal approach which includes an early attempt to classify works of art as one would hotels and detailed information on the costs of laundry work in Naples and the like. Later she lived in retirement at Exmouth, the animator of 'society' there, but died, in harness so to speak, at Milan on the way home from Naples. Her book was a pioneer work and reached at least eight London editions, many published by Murrays, as well as others put out in Leghorn and Paris.

The changed world circumstances saw four different developments: first, the systematic translation of the leading foreign guides (Ebel's Switzerland, Romberg's Brussels, Vasi's Rome, Reichard's itineraries), secondly the commissioning of new works (Boyce's Belgian traveller 1815, Campbell's Holland, Belgium and Germany 1818, Edward Planta's Paris, 1814); thirdly the evolution of other specialist firms such as Sherwood, Neely and Jones, Samuel Leigh, and eventually Murray; and lastly the rise of active foreign firms, often using destitute expatriates as authors, who provide detailed on-the-spot guides.[14] The most famous of the latter was the Paris firm of Galignani, whose shop in the Rue de Rivoli was only taken over by W. H. Smith relatively recently since even in the 1960s a last family member, Monsieur Jeancourt-Galignani, was still running the business. Galignani's bookshop and reading room, which published its own scissors and paste compendium of the Anglo-Saxon press right up to 1914, was the universal touch-down of every English or American traveller so that *Galignani's messenger* could most usefully report that Sir Walter Scott, Mr Fennimore Cooper or Mr Charles Dickens 'had left Paris for Switzerland [or wherever] yesterday' and similar locally collected news.[15] The Galignani *Picture of Paris*, later *New Paris guide*, equally came out virtually annually from Waterloo to 1914, thus chronicling in the most extraordinary fashion all the numerous changes and developments in Paris urban and cultural life over the whole century. The fate of foreign language publications is however not necessarily to be appreciated either abroad (because they are not in the local vernacular) or in the country of their language (because they are not published there): as a result, and despite its enormous factual interest, there is no complete run of the Galignani guide in any French, English or American library!

A small observation on the side: the emergence of the guide book market in the period 1760–1815 can perhaps be pinpointed by one particular aspect, the uniformity of size and binding of these productions. Kearsley's guides are rarely found leather-bound but are usually uncut and in half bindings with sheep spines and marbled paper boards. Once one has seen several one has no doubt that this was the accepted dress of the series: gentlemen took them around with them and, once home, had little further use for them thus not justifying the expense of binding. Samuel Leigh's post-Waterloo extensive series were equally clearly marketed as such: small dumpy pocket books, they were covered uniformly in blue sheep and given fancy lettering on their upper covers, thus being attractively visible on the table in the shop or in your hotel room. Every major nineteenth-century series, Murray's, Baedeker's etc, followed suite.

The time has come to take the final period, 1830 to 1870, as one. This is the high watermark of English tourism, of what one might term imperialism through tourism, the period when Switzerland for example becomes the very British 'playground of Europe', when some would claim the the British virtually invented skiing as a sport, when so many 'promenades' or 'cascades' suddenly became 'des Anglais', just as hotels were 'de Londres' or similarly 'de l'Angleterre'. All this was the result of a very intensive development of the tourist market, effected by locals and others, exploiting the new methods of mass travel, by coach, up the Rhine by boat, and later by train. The hotel and the resort world were born, the former word (*OED*: 'an establishment, especially of a comfortable or luxurious kind, where paying visitors are provided with accommodation, meals, and other services') being dated back to the mid-eighteenth century but branching out later to cover private hotels, residential hotels, family hotels and temperance hotels. Natural sights are opened up, galleries developed and exhibitions become all the rage. This situation is met on the guide-book front by an increasing professionalism, firms specialising further in this field and employing writers who equally travel around, inspect, judge, and reward with suitable publicity. Lastly the appearence of small local guides in the language of the principal visitors increases, in the case of the English often provided by Anglican clergy, who vary the tedium of their quiet rural English life as, say, the vicar of Somerford Parva, by spending the summer as curate of foreign, exotic and fashion-able Bad Ems. A map showing the dates of foundation of Anglican churches on the continent would be an excellent pointer to those places where there was a sizeable English population for at least part of the year. As it is I can record locally printed guides, in English, in, at least, Aix-la-Chapelle, Amsterdam, Antwerp, Arras, Berlin, Bonn, Boulogne, Brussels, Calais, Carlsbad, Copenhagen, Dieppe, Ems, Florence, Frankfort am Main, The Hague, Hamburg, Heidelberg, Milan, Rome, Rouen, Spa, Trieste, Venice, Versailles, Vienna, and Wiesbaden.

Five names, including two well-known ones and three lesser-known, must be mentioned. Firstly, of course, John Murray III whose *Handbook for travellers on the Continent*, covering Holland, Belgium, Prussia, northern Germany, and along the Rhine to Switzerland, first appeared in 1836, being rapidly followed by Southern Germany 1837; Switzerland proper 1838; Denmark, Norway, Sweden, Russia 1839; the Ionian Islands, Greece and Turkey 1840; Italy 1842, and by Richard Ford's Spain in 1845. Murray's guides have attracted much attention but one should note in passing that they were originally based, at least in part, on his own recollections, that they presented rearranged and thought-out routes, and that they were regularly revised and updated.

The two lesser-known series are those by Francis Coghlan, who may well have been a travel agent initially and whose early (1828) series starts with *A Guide to France; or, Travellers their own commissioners; shewing the cheapest and most expeditious system of travelling with hints on how to obtain their own passports,* a duodecimo of only 36 pages but in which series the Paris and Belgian guides reached at least 16 editions, apart from a host of other 'miniature' guides to special places or areas. Equally Alexander Tighe Gregory's series of 'Practical guides by an Englishman abroad' did well in the 1850s and 1860s. The 'miniature' and 'practical' emphasis of these series clearly reflected a market for lightweight volumes and the rise of the pedestrian tour (featuring, amongst other places, in Trollope's 1864 *Can you forgive her?*) is signalled by the existence of 'Knapsack' guides. Nor should one forget the Alpine urges, Christian or (like Shelley) other, which led not only to the trail blazing to, and conquest of, so many mountains (leading also to the creation of the profession of mountain guide) but also to the foundation of the Alpine Club (1857). The early members of the club including people like John Ball, the author of *Peaks, passes and glaciers* (1859), a work available on India paper and in small sections for easier and, above all, lighter use.

The last name is evidently that of Karl Baedeker, the exhaustive German publisher who challenged Murray's first moves into the guidebook field from as early as 1839. Like Murray, whom in the end he really superseded, Baedeker and his firm have been comprehensively bibliographised and studied. The first Baedeker to be translated into English was the Rhine volume of 1861. Baedekers were more serious and all-inclusive than Murrays, the firm did nothing else and slowly the primacy of the upper reaches of the more informative guidebook field became theirs. The period 1870 to 1914 has therefore righty been called 'the Age of Baedeker'.

One or two final points can be mentioned: first the bibliographical one that the title-page date is not always that of the issue of that particular copy. Guides were evidently not totally revised every year. The text was done now and then, in competitive fields doubtless more frequently than others, but the appendix on hotels and their prices was kept, often anually, up to date as a by-line to this final section will often reveal. One last evocative quotation: the 1873 reviewer of Murray's handbooks wrote:

The enormous extension of Continental travel is one of the great features of the last ten years. During the autumn months the whole of Europe seems to be in a state of perpetual motion. There is a mob at every small railway station. The new hotels (as at Lucerne) are built to receive 5, 6, or 700 guests, and those most frequented turn away daily some 200 applicants, for whom there is no room. Every spot, however difficult of access, is attacked. The remote lake Koenigsee, in Bavaria, to which perhaps a dozen strangers formerly found their way in the course of a month, now supports four boats, while the carriages waiting on the shore may be counted by fifties. The top of the Rigi is worn bare of grass, and is strewn with broken bottles and fragments of the *'Daily Telegraph'*; while here among the clouds 300 persons sit down daily to a *table d'hote* very well served.[16]

In summing up one should record that the most popular town destinations with their own particular guide appear to have been, in order, Paris, Boulogne, and Heidelberg. Overall therefore one can identify four periods: 1660–1690, the age of Italy and of the translation of foreign guides; 1690–1790, the period of development of the gentleman's guide; 1815–1840 the time of the development of the systematic, all-over guide produced by specialist publishers for a numerically growing market; and finally from 1840 onwards the evolution of both upper class, 'comfort and culture' guides such as Murray and Baedeker, and the simultaneous exploitation of a more popular, mass market. Publishers naturally reacted to the growth of, and the changes in, the travel and tourism markets. Guides proliferated and as new ones came out the old were, more often than with books, treated with scant respect. Old ones were disposed of and thus become rare, but those one can still find are not only often remarkable sources of period information, but also mirrors of contemporary values and habits, not to mention interesting, and often very rare, evidence for the history of both printing and publishing.

References

1. Robert Watt, *Bibliotheca Britannica; or A general index to British and foreign literature*, 4 vols, Edinburgh: 1824.

2. W. A. B. Coolidge, *Swiss travel and Swiss guide-books*, London: 1889. See also R. W. Clark's biography of Coolidge, *An eccentric in the Alps*, London: 1959.

3. Sir George Fordham, *Les routes de France*, Paris: 1929 (the Fordham Collection now being in the Royal Geographical Society's library), C. P. Brand, 'A bibliography of travel-books describing Italy published in England 1800–1850', *Italian studies*, XI, 1956, pp.108–17, R. S. Pine-Coffin, *Bibliography of British and American travel in Italy to 1860*, Florence: 1974, Ludwig Schudt, *Le guide di Roma*, Vienna: 1930 (later revised Pollak).

4. Jeremy Black, *The British abroad: the Grand Tour in the eighteenth century*, London: 1992, Greenwood Press, *Baedeker's Handbooks for travellers, a bibliography of English editions published prior to World War II*, Westport, Conn., 1975, and W. B. C. Lister, *A bibliography of Murray's handbooks for travellers*, Dereham: 1993, the latter being particularly useful for its brief biographies of the compilers.

5. William Carr, *An accurate description of the United Netherlands*, London: 1691, Prologue, p.[1].

6. Esmond de Beer, 'The development of the guide book until the early nineteenth century', *Journal of the British archaeological Association*, vol.15, 1952, pp.35–46.

7. Ludwig Schudt, *Le guide di Roma*, Vienna: 1930, no.58.

8. Andrew Boorde, *First book of the introduction of knowledge*, London: Early English Text Society, extra series 10, 1870, p.110.

9. Jonathan Richardson senior, *An account of some of the statues, bas-reliefs, drawings and pictures in Italy*, London: 1722, sig.a 5.

10. [Anon or attributed to the publisher, Thomas Taylor], *The Gentleman's Pocket Companion for travelling into Foreign parts*, London: 1722, sig.B4ᵛ, B5ᵛ.

11. London: Stationers' Company, *Entries of Copies* 1710–1842.

12. Information on Playstowe comes largely from the notes by Ron Browne and Maurice Packer in *Factotum* 20, 1985. In a forthcoming article I shall be dealing at length with Playstowe and his *Gentleman's Guide*.

13. For Naples see John Mazzinghi, *A guide to the antiquities and curiosities in the city of Naples and its environs*, Naples: for the author, 1817.

14. Johann Gottfried Ebel, *Traveller's guide through Switzerland*, London: S. Leigh, 1818; J. B.Romberg, *Brussels and its environs*, London: 1816; M. Vasi, *New picture of Rome*, London: S. Leigh, 1819; H. A. O. Reichard, *An itinerary of France and Belgium*, London: S. Leigh, 1816 etc.

15. See Giles Barber, 'Galignani's and the publication of English books in France from 1800 to 1852', *The Library*, 5th ser., vol.16 (1961), pp.267–86.

16. *The Edinburgh Review*, October 1873, p.497.

Illustrated books of the Middle East
1800–1850

CHARLES NEWTON

IN THE PERIOD FROM 1800 to 1850 a multiplicity of wonderfully illustrated books about the Middle East were produced in Britain and France, enough for a small but respectable library to be formed of them alone. The variety is bewildering, as they were produced for many different reasons and for a widely differing public. It is difficult now to grasp and make sense of this totality, but I am going to try, very briefly, to suggest some of the reasons for the explosion of interest and activity at the beginning of the nineteenth century and describe some of the techniques used to achieve it. I will also tentatively describe some of the ways to form categories within the broad definition of illustrated travel book, in the hope that one day a full study of these books in their context, and their reception at the time, can be made. Very briefly, to put them roughly into modern terms, these categories or areas of interest to the original readers were History, Anthropology, Romance and Religion. There are certainly many other ways of making categories, but these seem to me the simplest.

One of the problems of studying the books of this period is that they are often so beguiling that you lose sight of the greater picture almost at once. You take down the book from the shelf, open it at random, and an intriguing image catches your attention. The pictures, sometimes what is expected, sometimes outlandish, may be brilliantly coloured, and usually unfaded, if the book is still properly bound. They show a vanished world, which can now only be recreated with the aid of these images, and they often incorporate unexpected details, beyond the scope of the unaided imagination. The texts of the descriptions are to modern readers quaint, but elegant or romantic, and immediately, as you confirm the details of the traveller's words by comparison with the pictures, you are lost in the exploration of another land, another civilisation, and another time. You have already forgotten the much drier task of generalising in an academic way about the whole book, its classification and its context. The real difficulty is that they are too interesting.

An example of another difficulty is that there is no recent book that attempts an overview of the subject in the way that the great bibliophile and collector J. R. Abbey did. Any study of the subject must begin with his *Travel in Aquatint and Lithography 1770–1860 From the Library of J. R. Abbey A Bibliographical Catalogue*, 2 vols, 1956.[1] He had collected and studied a large number of these books, and obviously felt passionately about them. His catalogue is an indispensable, detailed and scholarly description of the books, and yet he did not speculate much about the context in which they were published. Indeed, why should he have done? He published his book as a guide mainly for other collectors and connoisseurs who already knew of the books, although not in such detail. He took for granted, as it was taken in those days, that the educated audience for his work would not want any help to understand the social history and background of that period. The shared assumptions in the old system of teaching history to the young created a large but limited pool of general knowledge that all educated people were supposed to possess. Things have changed and young students now simply do not have that specific general knowledge implicitly required by Abbey's book and the illustrated texts he describes as a bibliographer. There are further complexities as Abbey describes various editions of many books, caused by the publishers' difficulties in assembling and collating sometimes hundreds of illustrations made from copper plates or lithographic stones for a new edition.

The reasons for the production of so many books after 1800 must include the various revolutions that occurred not only in the material world, but also in the climate of thought in the latter part of the eighteenth century. The obvious candidates usually put forward are the Industrial Revolution (which we will come on to later under 'techniques') and the French Revolution and the consequent rise of Napoleon. His invasion of Egypt took place in that *annus mirabilis* of 1798, just over 200 years ago. Along with his soldiers he took with him a smaller army of Savants, scientists whose mission would be to draw and record Egypt ancient and modern. This they did, and produced the enormous work, published over many years, filled with splendid etchings and engravings, entitled *Description de l'Egypte*.[2] The idea was revolutionary, but the methods of illustration looked back to the mid-eighteenth century of Diderot's *Encyclopedie*.

1798 is also the year of two other major innovations, small in their beginnings but of great importance later. One was the publication of Wordsworth's *Lyrical Ballads* in 1798, which signalled the rise of a romanticism whose time had come. A new and bigger audience for romantic texts and pictures was fast forming. Meanwhile in Germany in 1798 Senefelder announced that he had invented a completely new form of autographic printmaking, that of lithography. *Autographic* means that what you draw on the stone, even broad-brush strokes, is what you get on the paper. There is no need for an engraver to interpret your work. Therefore a lithograph can be simple, direct and expressive immediately. It preserves (but only in the hand of a skilled artist) the sensitive and spontaneous movements of the brush, pencil or crayon. It is a technique ideally suited to the romantic idea of spontaneity. It took a few years to develop as a useful way of illustrating books, but by the late 1830s David Roberts and his lithographer Louis Haghe were famously exploiting it to the full in their illustrations to *The Holy Land, Syria, Idumea, Arabia, Egypt & Nubia* of 1842–9.[3]

However, as is so often the case, pioneering artists manage to achieve remarkable effects at the beginning of a new technique. For example, Louis Dupré produced an exquisite series of 40 hand-coloured lithographs in his book *Voyage à Athènes et à Constantinople*,[4] published in Paris as early as 1825, which are as good, or mostly better than, works made twenty years later.

Incidentally, lithography unwittingly led to the downfall of the ordinary artist-illustrated book. Joseph Nicephore Niepce, the inventor of photography, experimented first with the new lithography in the 1820s. He tried to photosensitise the surface of the stones and produce a fixed image from nature, with poor results. He went on to create the first photomechanical reproductive print in 1827 and the first fixed but blurred photographic image in a camera obscura in 1826. His son collaborated with Daguerre to invent the Daguerreotype in 1849. Fox Talbot at the same moment had developed his positive/negative system. Photography as we know it was born, and nothing was ever the same again. By the 1860s commercial ways of photomechanical printmaking were making artist printmakers' illustrations obsolete except for the precious 'livres d'artiste'. Even superb draughtsmen like Prisse d'Avennes started to use modified photographs in order to capture the details of Mamluk architecture, whereas his early books such as his *Oriental Album*[5] had exploited to the full the hand-drawn lithograph.

The late eighteenth century had also seen a great improvement to etching, an older form of printmaking. Aquatinting is essentially etching, plus a means of achieving an effect of subtle gradations of tone. It sounds complicated, but the net result is a picture which, when coloured by hand, can much more closely reproduce the effect of a watercolour. By 1800 book publishers were making full use of its splendid effects and continued to do so until the cheaper and less time-consuming hand-coloured lithographs finally ousted it in the 1820s. A vigorous and entertaining example is the naval officer and artist Francis B. Spilsbury's *Picturesque Scenery In The Holy Land And Syria, Delineated During The Campaigns Of 1799 and 1800*.[6] It is a volume of 20 plates with a descriptive text, published in 1803, 'sketched on the Spot by F. B. Spilsbury' in the course of the campaign against Napoleon.

Machine-made paper; another late eighteenth-century invention and product of the Industrial Revolution, brought down the price of illustrated books, as did improved printing presses. The wealth generated by this revolution enabled a far larger proportion of the expanding population in Britain to afford illustrated books.

These are only some of the ingredients for a bigger and more varied audience, and better books to satisfy the demand. I mentioned earlier an attempt to divide these books into tentative categories. The first I shall briefly mention is the Historic. One group of readers that had persisted from the eighteenth century were the antiquaries and connoisseurs, interested in the lavish folio illustrated with traditional etchings and engravings, concerned with a learned subject. The example of ancient buildings and their decoration might also be intended for practical use by those with an interest in architecture. Books about such historic sites as Palmyra and Petra continued the traditions of mid-eighteenth-century books like those of Stuart and Revett and Robert Adam, but there was an increasing interest in Egyptian antiquities. A typical early nineteenth-century example would be William Richard Hamilton's *Aegyptiaca*;[7] published 1809–10, and illustrated with etchings. Yet publications like these were an ever-dwindling proportion of the market as more popular books with high-quality illustrations were produced.

From the sixteenth century there had been a long tradition of books about foreign people, costumes and customs. This is roughly what I suppose we would now call anthropology. Here, in the nineteenth century the use of high-quality aquatint was particularly apposite. These books were meant for a different kind of public, those who were not necessarily scholars or connoisseurs, but newly wealthy people who were curious about other nations and how they compared with the workaday world they already knew. This readership of armchair travellers is still here, and explains the enduring popularity of Luigi Mayer's work as an illustrator of exotic places. His work is eagerly collected now and a study of why his appeal has endured, for different reasons at different times, would be a book in itself.

Mayer drew what his employer, Sir Robert Ainslie, the British Ambassador to Turkey in the 1790s, asked him to, and he also drew for his own pleasure and profit. So there are pictures of antiquities, but also modern Turkish and Egyptian life and costume, quaint customs, illustrations of the Bible lands and all kinds of oddities. His watercolours, and the aquatints made after them are colourful, lively and vigorously drawn. His widow Klara, herself an artist, arranged for his works to be aquatinted and published by Robert Bowyer and others in the first decade of the nineteenth century. Numerous versions and reprints of his and her work were published long into the nineteenth century, the latest one I have seen being William Watts, *Views Of Interesting Places In The Holy Land*,[8] in 1830. A note in the volume states that the views were copied accurately from *Views of Palestine or the Holy Land*,[9] after sketches by Ludwig Mayers [*sic*], with explanations by E. F. C. Rosenmeller. They were recycling Mayer's secular themes for a different and much duller didactic purpose, which will be examined below.

The next category is Romance. Byron and the rise of romanticism are synonymous. If in 1813 a reader had purchased John Cam Hobhouse's *A Journey Through Albania, and other Provinces of Turkey in Europe and Asia, to Constantinople, during the years 1809 and 1810*,[10] he would have seen the same exotic sights (illustrated as aquatints), such as the First Gate Of The Seraglio, that Byron certainly saw when he was in Albania and Turkey with Hobhouse. There is much about Byron's life that invites illustration, so Byron's publisher, John Murray, eventually decided to commission the Finden brothers to illustrate a book about him and his works. Edward Francis Finden and William Finden were leading engravers of their time, working both independently and jointly, who contributed illustrations to numerous publications. This particular joint venture was edited by William Brockedon and was entitled *Finden's Illustrations of the Life and Works of Lord Byron*,[11] and was published 1833–5. The Findens commissioned leading artists of the time, such as Turner and David Roberts, to provide sketches for them to engrave for this very successful book.

Another romantic publication was a magnificent volume of lithographs made by John Frederick Lewis in 1837 and published 1838. He did not actually visit Constantinople until 1840, but he was commissioned by Colnaghi to work up a series of sketches by a rather mediocre artist called John Coke Smyth. This book until very recently was a puzzle to me and to others as it describes itself as *Lewis's*

Illustrations of Constantinople.[12] The title-page states that *Lewis's Illus-trations* were 'made during a Residence in that City &c. in the Years 1835–6', that is, as if Lewis had lived and sketched there. Later this is apparently contradicted and it states that they were 'Arranged and Drawn on Stone from the original Sketches of Coke Smith by John F. Lewis.' Yet Lewis himself had not yet travelled to Constantinople. My view had been skewed because I had not thought about the customers for this book. There was a demand for the romantic places described by Byron coupled with the fact that Colnaghi needed to follow up the success of Lewis's *Sketches of Spain*,[13] lithographs of 1836, another deeply romantic place.

So successful had been Lewis's paintings and lithographs of Spain that he was thereafter known as 'Spanish' Lewis. But he was now back in foggy London. Colnaghi's short cut to cash in on the Spanish success was to bring the customers romantic Turkey at the hands of a young but now famous painter without the delay and expense of sending him there. Such was Lewis's skill in rendering life-like versions of Coke Smyth's sketches, that some modern collectors actually conjectured that Lewis must have been to Constantinople before he in fact did so. However, there are slight errors in rendering the architecture which give the game away. Modern collectors of orientalist imagery had not realised the selling point in 1836 was mainly Mr Lewis the famous artist's romantic vision, not a desire for a literal topographical rendering of the Turkish capital and its environs. That was a job instead for the panorama makers.

The next category is that of Religion which in Britain at that time mostly meant the Bible. Everyone then knew their Bible, and many were curious about the places mentioned in the Scriptures, particularly as the explosion of travellers penetrating the East had already produced a good crop of first-hand accounts of the holy places as they now appeared. (In the period between 1800 and 1878, a minimum of 2,000 authors published books on Palestine.) Thus the publisher John Murray, already secure in the knowledge that there had been a large audience eager for an earlier publication illustrated by the Findens, decided to publish volumes devoted to the Bible. This book was eventually published as *Landscape Illustrations of the Bible*, 1836, with a text by the Revd T. H. Horne.[14]

Given that in the 1830s there was a rapidly expanding literate public, who were mostly middle-class churchgoers, and more desirous of respectability than their Regency forebears, it was a good choice. The only major problem was that of rival publications devoted to similar themes, trying to cash in at the same moment. Typical books issued in rivalry were John Carne's *Syria, The Holy Land, Asia Minor, &c.* 1837–8,[15] and Revd Robert Walsh's *Constantinople and the scenery of the Seven Churches of Asia Minor* 1838–40.[16]

These books encapsulate the progress and contradictions of nineteenth-century taste. First there was the wicked Regency hero, Lord Byron, dashing and romantic, still in vogue in the 1830s. The demand for the romantic pictures (often views in Italy and the Middle East) to accompany the poetry and drama of Byron's works suggested to Murray that there was another, even bigger audience. This readership might not want the reprobate's sceptical and pagan works, but instead might buy a book of romantic but harmless and improving pictures of the landscape of belief with a safer text. A child at Sunday school could be shown the images in *Landscape Illustrations...* even if they could not read or understand the words, and the most educated, pious and elderly would find the tasteful interpretations of the sketches of a Turner or David Roberts a useful accompaniment to belief.

So the Findens had started by exploiting sceptical Regency romanticism, which was fast becoming less respectable, and went on to the certainties of the Biblical landscape. In 1832–3, Sir Augustus Wall Callcott, with William Turner, David Roberts, Clarkson Stanfield and James Duffield Harding, and other well-known and established artists were commissioned by John Murray to provide drawings for this series of prints illustrating Biblical scenery. The 37 or so artists, some of whom provided the initial sketches, and others who worked them up for the engravers to copy, were a very varied group. For example, they included Louis Cassas, a French painter and engraver who worked in Syria, Turkey, Egypt and the Lebanon, C. R. Cockerell the architect who had travelled as a young man on the grander tour of Greece, Turkey and the Holy Land, Frederick Catherwood, an architectural draughtsman who had drawn the antiquities of Egypt, Selina Bracebridge, an amateur who made watercolour sketches of her travels, and the diplomat and traveller James Morier who was famous as the author of *The Adventures of Hajji Baba of Ispahan.*

Of course, most of the more famous artists had not actually been to the Holy Land, but were asked to use sketches from other travellers. Some of the travellers were good artists in their own right, such as Sir Charles Barry, the future architect of the Houses of Parliament, who early in his career had made the on-the-spot sketch of Mount Moriah that Turner used for his drawing. Edward Finden used the 'Turnerised' sketch of Barry as the direct source for his etching. Other prints do not have quite such an illustrious pedigree. A most illuminating sequence is that leading up to the penultimate image entitled 'Sardis. One of the Seven Churches.'

It is worth examining this print in some detail for the light it casts on Victorian book illustration generally. The initial on-the-spot sketch by a 'Mr Maude' (whoever he was) still exists; it is in the Searight Collection at the Victoria & Albert Museum. To tell the truth, it is a rather dull but competent amateur ink and wash sketch of the only two columns still standing of the Temple of Artemis, with no figures or anything of emotional interest. William Finden then gave Clarkson Stanfield this unprepossessing drawing to 'work up' and do his best with.

Sardis, now Sart in modern Turkey, was a desolate spot then, with only a few ruins as a pathetic remnant of the fabulous wealth of one of the Seven Churches of Asia admonished in the Apocalypse, the Revelation of St John the Divine. Presumably this sketch was the only authentic representation that the Findens could obtain. Stanfield duly used it as the starting point of his own painting (also in the Searight Collection), but immediately made it into a dramatic watercolour, rivalling his contemporary John Martin, by introducing a thunderstorm and a rider who has been thrown down by his horse, panicked by the apocalyptic weather. The finished print in the book is a fairly faithful version of this dramatic improvement. It was not merely a picture of some ruins; the image referred to the fulfilment of a Biblical prophecy, which actually looked forward to the final days, the terrible moment of God's Last Judgement. Only an artist's imagination could transform Mr Maude's record drawing into a visual sermon.

The prints themselves are usually described generically as 'engravings' and the Findens as 'Engravers'. In fact the prints that they excelled in producing are mostly very fine etching, a quicker and freer medium than the laborious technique of engraving, where one small image might take many weeks of intensive work.

Many Victorians subsequently formed their mental pictures of the Holy Land on these small illustrations, modifying their imagined views of the Jordan, Jerusalem and Bethlehem, which they had tentatively formed as they had listened to and then read the Scriptures for themselves. The paradox is that the etchings are in black and white, and they were not intended to be hand-coloured, so that the brilliant colours of the Stanfield sketch had to be provided solely in the imagination of the readers. Now that the modern world is filled with complete colour images of every kind and size, it is hard to grasp and to remember that our ancestors saw relatively few illustrations in colour. Thus they had to rely solely on their imaginations to fill the gaps in a way, and to an extent, that is difficult now to comprehend.

There was a keen appreciation of the fine details of the etchings, sharpened by the fact that illustrations of any kind were so few in comparison with our image-glutted age. As we now contemptuously throw away a junk-mail catalogue, we do not consider that we are disposing of perhaps a thousand individual high-resolution colour images. These cheap and disposable images would have astounded an illustrator who had laboured many hours to achieve just one reproductive image before the invention of reliable photomechanical reproduction.

British travellers became more and more frequent in the region, something that John Murray and other publishers were not slow to exploit, providing travel guides as well as travel books in general for the increasing flow of tourists as the century progressed. Following this vogue for travel, a surge of illustrated books was published, but the first real anthology of views of the Holy Land was *Landscape Illustrations…* It set a precedent for many other publications. Today the best known are by David Roberts, whose hand-coloured lithographs were published in *The Holy Land, Syria, Idumea, Arabia, Egypt & Nubia* of 1842–9, already mentioned. He had travelled in 1838 to Egypt and Syria, inspired, it is said, by his work for the Findens.

There are literally hundreds of books which could have been mentioned in addition to a few of the most famous alluded to here. I have tried to suggest why there were so many, and what kinds of need they fulfilled. In the 50 years after 1800, magnificent print-making techniques were used by the most skilled artists to produce delightful books, which are now more eagerly collected than ever. I must also try to suggest why they generally declined after 1850. One answer is obvious: the rise of cheaper photography and photomechanical illustrations. Photography may or may not be Art, but it was recognised from its foundation as a new branch of printmaking. (One name proposed for this new invention by its pioneers was 'Solar Mezzotint'.) People were seduced by the apparent total reality of representation that photography seemed to offer. On more mature reflection, it is now obvious that nineteenth-century photographs, at least, distorted reality in their own way. Compare an 1825 colour aquatint view of, say, the main gate of the Sultan's Palace in Constantinople, with the Fountain of Ahmed III in the foreground, with an 1860s photograph of the same subject. The aquatint is very selective but colourful and full of life while the black and white photograph seems dreary in comparison. The lack of colour emphasises the dust and dereliction, the cracks in the masonry and the poverty of the street traders. The aquatint tells lies, as it were, leaving out the bad bits, betraying the eagerness of the artist to represent his positive feelings of admiration for the polychrome decoration of the fountain and the lively scenes of daily life that go on around it.

Before 1850, people generally wanted a view of something they had never seen which actually related to the way they imagined it. Thus they preferred the romantic recreations of an apocalyptic scene of Sardis by Clarkson Stanfield to a literal and emotion-free representation of dusty ruins by Mr Maude. Yet photographs were so seductive that they changed the perception of the world and affected the imagination in ways we cannot now measure.

The scientific literalness of the later nineteenth century, whatever its causes, also contributed to the popular preference for photography. The boom in tourism and the increasing accessibility of the Middle East meant that later nineteenth-century visitors could feed their own imaginations on-the-spot, and carry away a photograph as an *aide-mémoire*. In a sense, the wheel has come full circle, for we now cannot visit those places so eloquently delineated by the artists in the early nineteenth century. They have changed so profoundly under the impact of the modern world that the only way to see them as they were is in the imagination with the aid of those wonderful illustrated books that delighted our ancestors.

References

1. J. R Abbey, *Travel in Aquatint and Lithography 1770–1860 From the Library of J. R. Abbey. A Bibliographical Catalogue*, 2 vols, London: privately printed at the Curwen Press, 1956. Books described by Abbey will be cited with the Abbey catalogue number. However, there are many possible variations in the number order and states of the prints that form the illustrations in books of this period, thus often a particular volume does not match Abbey's description exactly.

2. *Description de l'Egypte*. 19 vols publiée par C. L. F. [Panckoucke]. Paris: 1809–22

3. Abbey, 272 and 385

4. Louis Dupré, *Voyage à Athènes et à Constantinopole; ou, Collection de portraits, de vues et de costumes grecs et ottomans, peints sur les lieux, d'après nature, lithographiés et coloriés … accompagné d'un text orné de vignettes*. Paris: [s.n.], 1825.

5. Achille-Constant-Théodore-Emile Prisse D'Avennes, *Oriental Album. Characters, Costumes, And Modes Of Life, In The Valley Of The Nile*. London: James Madden, 1848.

6. Abbey, 381.

7. William Richard Hamilton FAS, *Remarks on Several Parts of Turkey*. London: T. Payne, Cadell and Davies, 1809–10.

8.   William Watts, *Views Of Interesting Places In The Holy Land*. Philadelphia: American Sunday School Union, [1830].
9.   Abbey, 369–71.
10. Abbey, 202.
11. William Brockedon, *Finden's Illustrations of the Life and Works of Lord Byron*. 3 vols. London: John Murray, 1833–5.
12. Abbey, 394.
13. Abbey, 149–50.
14. The Revd Thomas Hartwell Horne BD, *Landscape Illustrations of The Bible*. London: John Murray, 1836.
15. John Carne, *Syria, The Holy Land, Asia Minor, &c. Illustrated*. London: Fisher, Son and Co. [1837–8].
16. The Revd Robert Walsh LLD, *Constantinople and the Scenery of the Seven Churches of Asia Minor*. London: Fisher, Son & Co., [1838–40].

Bound for Australia:
shipboard reading in the nineteenth century

BILL BELL

> Readers are travellers; they move across lands belonging to
> someone else, like nomads poaching their way across the fields
> they did not write.
> Michel de Certeau, *The Practice of Everyday Life*

IN THE FIFTY YEARS between 1830 and 1880 no fewer than a million and a
half free emigrants embarked on the long voyage from Britain to
Australia. The three months' passage that followed would prove for some
to be the most difficult time of their lives; for others, it would represent
the longest period of enforced leisure that they would ever again enjoy.
Among the several cultural practices to which the nineteenth-century
shipboard emigrant turned for compensation, diversion, and in some
instances survival, reading would prove to be one of the most significant.[1]

It is perhaps no coincidence that the great wave of nineteenth-century
emigration was to occur at a time of conspicuously growing literacy. The
causes of emigration and improvement are explicitly associated in much of
the rhetoric of the period. David McKenzie advised his Australian-bound
audience in 1851 that they might profitably employ their time on the
long voyage 'in reading what will improve your heart and mind also … in
order to keep up with what is contemptuously styled the "march of
intellect"'.[2] John Mathison was also to remark in his *Counsel for
Emigrants* (1834) that the kinds of books that could now be purchased for
less than a shilling not only afforded 'information and amusement for the
Emigrant' but were in themselves evidence of the 'perfection to which
cheap literature is brought'.[3]

One of the most popular sources of information for the emigrant
reader in the nineteenth century was *Chambers's Edinburgh Journal*. Intended 'for the express use of the *poor man*', the magazine would offer,
according to its 1832 prospectus, 'a continued flow of valuable and correct
information for his guidance, should he be disposed or necessitated to
emigrate.'[4] *Chambers's* was one of scores of self-help publications which

Fig. 1. Matron reading aloud. *Emigrant tracts* no.III – *Hints to matrons of emigrant ships.* (1850). By courtesy of the National Library of Australia.

by the 1840s were being produced annually for a growing emigrant market. Typical of the genre were titles like P. B. Chadfield's *Out at Sea; or, the Emigrants Afloat,* advertising itself as a 'handbook of practical information for the use of passengers on a long sea voyage' and offering advice on matters from the choice of suitable berth and the preparation of luggage to the daily routine that could be expected on board.[5] More substantial was *Tegg's Handbook for Emigrants* (1839), a pocket-sized survival manual 'intended for Colonists ... dependent on themselves for the conveniences and comforts of life' which ran to over 200 pages, including advice on a range of skills including carpentry, cookery, and the performance of surgical operations. In response to the growing demand for amusing as well as instructive texts, a number of publishers were also to repackage existing titles for use at sea. In 1851 the SPCK recommended a series of wholesome books 'suitable as parting gifts', including cheap editions of *Robinson Crusoe,* Bingley's *Eminent Voyagers, The Book of Boats,* and P. H. Gosse's *The Ocean.*[6] Those who had the means could even purchase before departure a complete cabinet library for use at sea.[7] By 1850, the Religious Tract Society was providing, for the cost of 20 shillings each, three box libraries 'for the service of seamen', each comprising 15 volumes of 'Practical Theology, Biology, History, and General Information'.[8] The most popular of these was probably the Chambers Popular Library. Advertised in 1855 as 'a selection of amusing and instructive reading, well adapted for Private Families, Emigrants, Ships' Libraries, &c.', it was available in four versions, each containing two Scott novels, several volumes of *Chambers's Information for the People*, and a variety of travel, history, and biography.

As well as providing the most reliable source of information for survival in the unknown, such texts also offered a potential diversion from the inevitable boredom of the long voyage. While advising his readers to dispose of all furniture before departure in view of high freight charges, one authority remarked that 'as many books as can be contained will afford amusement and instruction on the voyage.'[9] 'Before it is too late', yet another advised his readers, 'we would warn emigrants to provide against solitude by securing to themselves the intercourse of books, of which the best also happen to be the cheapest.'[10]

To the Promised Land

Shipboard is your place of study. Consider every hour valuable, and diligently employ it in reading or meditation.... In ancient times, those who went down to the sea in ships might no doubt have seen great wonders in the deep, for everything was then new, and before the art of printing ... the information of mankind was very limited; but *tempora mutuantur*, – for neither the *Penny Encyclopaedia* nor *Chambers's Information for the People* was then known.[11]

In the face of such exhortations, it is sadly ironic that the majority of emigrants would not have been in any position to enjoy such luxuries. Many in fact were actively discouraged from taking on board anything considered surplus to requirement. One agency advised steerage passengers in 1842 that their baggage should consist 'only of their wearing apparel, with such bedding and utensils for cooking as may be required on the voyage'.[12] Still another urged in 1853 that they could only 'take out with them the necessary tools of their trades that are not bulky' while 'large packages and extra baggage, if it can be taken at all, must be paid for'.[13] According to David Vincent, it was rare for the poor, particularly those in rural areas, to own more than a handful of books.[14] Given the prohibitive cargo allowance (a mere 20 cubic feet per steerage passenger bound for Australia in the 1850s), with houses to build and furnish, children to feed and clothe, and crops to plant, it is unlikely that many

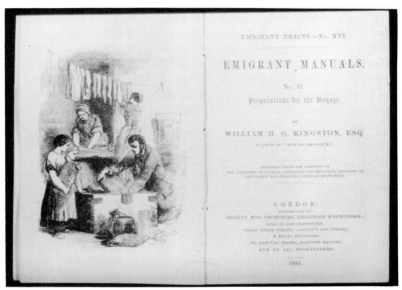

Fig.2. Emigrant tracts no.XVI – *Emigrants' Manuals* no.II. *Preparations for the Voyage.* (1851).
By courtesy of the National Library of Australia.

books beyond the Bible and prayer-book – perhaps the odd volume of *Pilgrim's Progress* – would have found their way on the voyage.

None was to exploit this captive audience more effectively than the many pious religious and charitable organisations that sprang up from the 1830s, part of a vast institutional apparatus that was put in place for the intellectual and moral improvement of the emigrant poor. The most prolific distributor of edifying literature on land and sea was the Society for Promoting Christian Knowledge which, by the 1860s, was providing over 8,000,000 items annually, among them a series of tracts issued specifically for distribution to Australian emigrants. Recommended by the British Ladies' Female Emigrant Society 'as a most valuable parting gift to such as are about to quit their native land', copies were routinely disseminated at major emigration depots before embarkation and given out freely by charitable organisations on board before departure. Among the many organisations that circulated the 'Emigrant Tracts' series was the Plymouth Emigrant Employment Society, the representatives of which distributed a 'general use bag' to the head of each mess on board the 'Joseph Somes' before its departure for Adelaide in 1850: 'These important functionaries also received a slate and, as an aid in fulfilment of their duties, a tract written expressly for the single men of emigrant ships, entitled "Hints for the Improvement of the Outward Passage", published by the Christian Knowledge Society.'[15]

Unmarried women, however, provided a particular focus for the energies of religious organisations. *Preparations for the Voyage* (1851) was one of many tracts from the period dedicated to informing female readers of their colonial domestic responsibilities:

Of vast importance to the prosperity and moral well-being of a colony is the influence which virtuous and well-educated women may exert over the newly assembled population.... Woman has a mission in Australia which she only can fulfil to civilize and reform the community, and in which the more educated and refined must also take their part.[16]

The austerity of conditions in the colony, it was felt, would further justify a clear moral division of labour between the sexes, a world where women were to bring morality and civilisation while their men were to get on with the more important business of taming the landscape.

By the 1850s an army of volunteers had been mobilised to provide daily instruction to unmarried females on government ships. The arrangement of single women into 'industrial classes' began at the depot even before departure, and before anchors were weighed there began a systematic daily round of reading, sewing, and prayers, all of which continued under the vigilant eye of the matron throughout the voyage. As *A Letter to Young Female Emigrants* (1851) admonished its readers:

As you can never again hope to have such a period of leisure, make the most of it. I would advise you to spend the mornings, until dinner time, in reading, writing, and cyphering: in the afternoon collect together in groups, and while one reads aloud, let the others work; you will be surprised to find how much information and profit you will derive from this systematic arrangement of your time.[17]

Motivated by a firm commitment to the proverbial belief that idle hands make mischief, many authorities were keen to engender high levels of intensive reading within the female quarters. Insisting on 'habits of order, industry, and cleanliness' a matron's principal responsibility was to ensure that her charges' time did not pass 'unimproved and unemployed'.[18] Among the more systematic attempts to habituate reading was *The Emigrant's Friend; Or, Scriptural Instruction for the Voyage* (1851), containing 'a series of Lessons for every Week of a Four months' Voyage', each including a biblical commentary to be read and Scripture verses to be memorised during the week.[19] The lengths to which such forms of social organisation could be carried is evident from the following report issued by the British Ladies' Female Emigrant Society in 1850:

The management of the Sunday was this – at half-past seven A.M. prayer class – half-past eight, breakfast – half-past nine, Roman Catholic prayers in the single women's apartment, no one being present but those belonging to that persuasion – eleven A.M. general muster on deck – quarter-past eleven, Church of England divine service; those of different persuasion being between decks. Service was over at quarter-past twelve. One P.M. dinner. Sunday school began at two and was over at five, tea at quarter-past five, and the remainder of the evening was spent in reading moral and religious books, and singing hymns. The good order and regularity observed on board, were entirely owing to the religious and moral teaching the emigrants received during the voyage.[20]

Despite these and other efforts to encourage the right kind of reading, the environment of the ship was not always conducive to long periods of study. Spending most of her time below deck, the steerage passenger was often subjected to poor lighting, nauseating smells, and constant movement, all of which are frequently referred to in personal correspondence and diaries. As cabin passenger William Johnstone observed in 1841, 'the between decks where the Emigrants were all stowed away (sometimes a man and his wife and two children in the one bed) were in a most horrible condition'. As the storm ensued, the same observer was to witness 'boxes … all adrift, flying about from one side to the other, with nearly 50 whining sick squalling children to complete their misery'.[21]

Even in relatively calm weather, long periods of concentration could be made difficult by peer pressure which militated against overt displays of literacy among less well-to-do passengers. If, as Richard Altick remarks, common readers in Victorian working-class communities were often 'subjected to the ridicule, or at best the well-meant disapproval, of those who failed to share one's inclination', how much more would similar social pressure be brought to bear in the close confines below deck.[22] Passengers on more than one Australian-bound ship were subjected to ridicule for the time they spent reading and writing.[23]

Perhaps the greatest obstacle to reading was the lack of light between decks. The author of one emigrant manual was perhaps being unduly optimistic when he informed his readers that a lantern could be routinely hung within reach of every berth, making it 'convenient to be able to light the lamp without getting out of bed.'[24] In the better quarters there were no doubt plentiful supplies of candles and oil lamps; in other cases inferior light had sometimes to be contrived by rendering down animal fat into a tin with cotton wool serving for a wick.[25] On some occasions, what little light existed was withdrawn as a means of punishing misdemeanours. All of the single women on board one 1849 government ship, it was reported, were 'sent below at eight o'clock and their lamp taken away and lockd up in the dark untill seven next morning'.[26] No more than six candles were shared by all of the women on the 'Hereford' as it travelled between Plymouth and Melbourne in 1853. Elizabeth Britton spent most of the voyage below deck where 'the doctor says there are to be no singing or any disturbance ... after 8 o'clock, so I suppose we must sit with our fingers in our mouths as there is not sufficient light with which to read or work'.[27]

Among the Gentiles

A vulgar people ... taxed to send away their blooming youth and maidens, after due examination in rows by the catechism of the clergyman and the microscope and stethoscope of the surgeon! A gallant navy, manned by model seamen, officered by Honourable Toms, Sir Harrys, and others not able to find place in the army, navy, excise, or customs, conducting a band of poor, but genteel, cabin passengers across the waters, to where money, land, and houses await their gracious acceptance – beguiling the wearisomeness of the passage by teaching the contented clowns in the steerage *manners* in calms and *resignation* in storms.[28]

Thus Samuel Sidney was to describe the organised effort to proselytise the poor in the face of such physical privation. Similar reservations were frequently voiced by poor emigrants themselves. Taking a sardonic view of attempts to edify steerage passengers, James Iles, a Scottish binder travelling on board the 'Chile' to Dunedin in 1866, remarked that the surgeon's attempt to read the sabbath service was little more than 'a burlesque of sacred things', while the distribution of tracts was conducted 'with outside show that they were very anxious about our eternal welfare, when, in fact, they cared for but little for our temporal wants'.[29] Even the devout Isabella Ritchie, who travelled on board the 'Nelson' bound for Port Chalmers in 1863, thought the sabbath reading 'such a mimicry of God's worship I never saw or heard of', reporting that 'they read us the history of some emigrant which I did not relish ... a bundle of inconsistencies'.[30]

Such propaganda, both at home and abroad, was to generate widespread mistrust of the printed word among working-class communities. 'The whole idea of reading was associated in many poor people's minds with the tract-distributors', observes Altick, 'and as a result the printed word became a symbol of their class's degradation.'

While readers might have preferred chapbooks to religious pamphlets, they would nevertheless accept narrative tracts 'if nothing better was to be had'.[31] Such reluctant acts of reading would have been even more likely at sea, where a combination of factors – boredom, the relative scarcity of printed matter, and the perceived danger of the journey – combined to make the use of even the most overtly moralistic text almost irresistible. Where an alternative was available, however, the emigrant would more often than not reject prescribed reading. The majority of males on board the 'Prestonjee Bomanjee' in 1854 were, according to its schoolmaster, 'men who would sit for hours reading a book' but were nevertheless entirely 'indisposed to attend school'. With an unusually catholic library at their disposal, the most popular categories appear to have been 'History, Biography, Travels, Tales, and above all books treating of the Colonies. The exclusively religious books the people will not read; they are therefore useless for the purpose intended.'[32] A similarly reluctant reader was William Calder, a compositor who had worked for Constables of Edinburgh and as a pressman at the *Scotsman* before his departure for South Australia in 1858. When, after two months into the voyage the ship's library was opened for the first time, Calder remarked: 'They are a parcel of old rubbish, several of them published in 1830, and on every subject except the ones most likely to be instructive or even amusing.' Speculating on the library's origins, he suspected that it had been 'got up of the clearings of several booksellers'.

For all of the heavy-handed attempts to proselytise the emigrant poor, private diaries and correspondence offer many such examples of readerly resistance, providing evidence that common readers were in fact far more sophisticated in their use of print than is sometimes thought, real readers resembling anything but the subjects interpellated by the texts themselves. But in citing such acts of resistance are we looking at unusually literate and self-confident individuals? We may well wonder whether such levels of literate response to official print culture were common among emigrant passengers. While literacy levels at sea, as on land, could vary enormously it can often be assumed that the level of an individual's literacy corresponded, more often than not, with his or her motives for emigration. It is quite clear, for instance, that the search by many for opportunities overseas was for many part of an overall attitude towards social aspiration and personal ambition. More than one historian has observed that those who sought a new life in Australia tended to be more entrepreneurial than those who remained at home, and therefore more inclined to be committed to notions of self-improvement. It was often with some surprise that cabin passengers remarked on the good manners and appearance of those below. Reverend John Smith noted in 1839 that the education and deportment of the passengers between the decks of the 'Amelia' were in fact far superior to those he had observed in the second-class cabins. Another minister remarked in 1852 on how astonished he was 'to find so many well dressed respectable looking people as steerage passengers in an emigrant ship'.[33]

Such was rarely the case of those who were part of the vast exodus of forced migration, most notably those casualties of the famines and clearances who, in the cases of Ireland and the West of Scotland, found themselves, as participants in non-anglophone oral cultures, outside accepted forms of literacy. Particularly well documented is the case of the party of Highland emigrants who travelled from Skye on board the 'Hercules' in 1853. When, on embarkation, all passengers were examined for their ability to read and write, of the 109 married men only four could read and write well according to the schoolmaster's report, while 43 exhibited varying levels of skill in reading and writing, ranging from the categories of 'tolerable' to 'indifferent'. 62 of the 109 could neither read nor write. Almost invariably, women fared worse than men. Of the 109 married females none could read nor write 'well', eight read 'indifferently', while 95 could 'neither read nor write'. Thus began a rigorous civilisation campaign, beginning with daily compulsory school lessons for all passengers, with in the evenings the encouragement of reading through the distribution of:

Bibles, Testaments & Psalm Books, as well as Tracts. Pamphlets and other Periodicals, both in Gaelic and English, suited to the capacities of the recipients. On Sabbath evenings, the monitors and I went round to exchange Tracts, &c, and by these means, these religious books, adapted for Sunday reading, were kept in circulation, and placed within the reach of all those that could read them....

On Friday evenings there were circulated from the ship's library

such books as were not of an educational character, to be read during the week – these were duly returned, and kept in circulation, in the same way as the Tracts, &c were, for Sunday Reading – In this manner the interest of the people was kept alive, and thereby a good stimulus given for their intellectual culture, and this was more pleasing, when the means of gratifying this desire of reading was placed within their reach.

When the 'Hercules' eventually arrived in Adelaide – a remarkable eight months later – it was reported that although there had been some initial resistance from the single women and two or three of the older women 'who had no desire to learn', the educational regime had led to a considerable improvement overall. Other official sources relating to Highland emigrants were to issue similarly positive reports. The agent on board the 'Bengal Merchant' which carried Highlanders to the 'first Scottish colony' in New Zealand in 1839 related with unrestrained pride that 'through the efforts of Missionaries in preaching, catechising, teaching to read and write & cipher, and circulating the Scriptures & tracts printed in the native tongue they are becoming more & more enlightened & brought under the influence of Christian civilization'.[34]

The fact that literacy was so intimately bound up with ideas of morality in the nineteenth century becomes curiously problematic when it comes to that most maligned of nineteenth-century exiles, the transportation convict. Subscribing to the wide-spread assumption that the colony was coming to civilise itself out of its notorious past, European settlers were keen to distance themselves from Australia's penal origins throughout the second half of the nineteenth century. It was with some satisfaction that Thomas McCombie reflected in 1850 on how a society 'composed of free emigrants and their descendants' was at last coming to acquire 'a tone of refinement.... Many of the former convicts were remarkably fortunate, and their former degraded position has not been regarded as an insuperable bar to the social advancement of their children.'[35] The fact was, of course, that many convicts were drawn from anything but the 'uncivilised' orders. Included in the transportation lists are skilled workers, retailers, political dissenters, disgraced schoolmasters, and even defrocked clergymen. It might, after all, be argued that the conception of felonies such as fraud, forgery, and embezzlement – even if unsuccessfully executed – required at least a certain level of respectability and intelligence.

J. D. Forbes, Guard Captain on board the 'Guildford', was appalled at the high rate of literacy he encountered *en route* to Sydney in 1827. On the first sabbath at sea Forbes observed the 'convict boys on quarter deck reading responses – very orderly and well behaved – read well enough to pretend great devotion'. A fortnight later he again noted: 'By the bye I observed today that every one of the convict boys can read – so much for the education of the lower orders.'[36] Although official evidence must be handled with caution, the accounts of ship's surgeons, who were responsible for keeping such records, would suggest that in many instances literacy rates on convict ships could be considerably higher than on government emigrant vessels. Of the 301 prisoners bound for Western Australia on board the 'Clara' in 1864 only 35, it appeared, could neither read nor write. According to the surgeon on board the 'Clyde' in the previous year only one of the 320 convicts on board was 'uneducated'.[37]

While physical conditions on board transport ships could be the most brutalising, there is evidence to suggest that the cultural life of their passengers could sometimes be far from unsophisticated. The diary of one convict provides a fairly detailed account of life between the decks of the 'Hougomont' as it made its way from London to Western Australia in 1867. Entertainments included a debating society, recitations from Shakespeare, nightly theatricals, and the publication of a weekly journal containing original poetry, critical articles, and a lively correspondence column. And it would be difficult to imagine a company of more erudite passengers than those responsible for the production of *The Voice of Our Exiles*, a weekly newspaper published in manuscript on board the 'Clara', the Prospectus of which appeared in February 1864:

In the words of Seneca composed in the evening of a brilliant tho' checquered career, we find the following aphorism – "Si tempus insterdium conferis, omne vitae fastidi un effugeris". "You must devote your time to study – if you would escape all the weariness of life". A Philosopher, a moralist and a man of the world, he had experienced the strangest vicissitudes of fortune. Of servile birth, he raised himself by the sheer force of his talents.... literary culture is able to mitigate the evils of servitude, and ... Rank and wealth without it, are no barrier against a monotonous and discontented existence.[38]

For several columns the editor continues in the same vein, drawing on a range of sources including Ovid, Boethius, Cervantes, and Bacon, presumably from memory. One of a series of highly sophisticated intellectual debates that goes on throughout the journal's pages relates to the penal code itself, the final editorial concluding:

According to the principles laid down by Jeremy Bentham, and recognised in all modern Codes of Law, Secondary Punishment must contain two primary elements – the one of a reforming, the other of a deterring nature – both of them designed to act in an equal degree on the Criminal, and the latter also intended to operate on the mind of the Community to which he belongs. There is moreover involved in all Punishment, a third element – the idea of expiation.

The question therefore resolves itself into the following ones. Does the present system, taken as a whole, contain these three indispensable conditions? Secondly – Does any part of the present system contain them? Thirdly – Is it possible to devise a system which may contain them?

To their solution we believe that hitherto a wrong method has been applied.

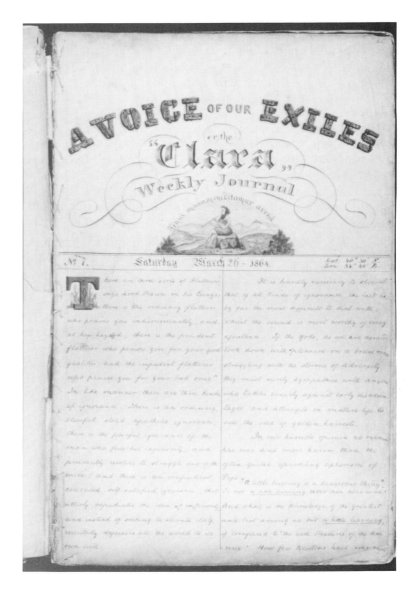

Fig.3. 'A Voice of Our Exiles. The Clara Weekly journal'. (1864) By courtesy of the National Library of Australia.

In this most unlikely of cultural contexts, *conspicuous literacy* could apparently still confer a degree of social status in the face of other forms of deracination. Dickens's Magwitch was not the only one, it seems, to take revenge on the society that had condemned him by making himself a 'gentleman'.

The Chosen Few

In his 1848 *Handbook for New Zealand*, E. J. Wakefield provided a detailed catalogue of items that he believed should accompany every 'good Colonist'. Under the general heading of 'BOOKS, MAPS, and ENGRAVINGS' readers were advised:

Every person who intends to adopt New Zealand as his future home will take care to supply himself with a good collection of these cheerful companions.... Arrangements can easily be made after arrival and settlement in the colony for the formation of book-clubs, to be supplied periodically with such new publications as they may desire. Before starting, each family should arrange so as to receive regularly a file of some weekly London paper. Those which, like the *Spectator*, *Examiner*, and *Athenaeum*, contain full notices of literary, dramatic, and musical subjects, are the most satisfactory to a colonist.

That Wakefield was writing for the well-heeled cabin passenger is apparent from his recommendation that 'the Colonist who is anxious to carry with him the memorials of the Fine Arts of the old world, may do so at comparatively little cost by purchasing at the British Museum casts in plaster of the antiques contained in that institution', some of which could be easily 'conveyed to the colony … at little cost, affording very tasteful ornaments, whether for the public buildings or for the larger rooms of private residences.'[39] Wakfield's intended audience, more 'colonist' that 'emigrant', was to be the exemplary carrier of high-brow culture for whom reading was clearly an indispensable means of preserving polite values far from home.

Such social aspirations demonstrate something of the extent to which conditions between classes could vary in a colonial context. The same socio-economic stratifications that governed life on land were apparent at sea, often more dramatically so. On his way to New Zealand, one steerage passenger informed his family: 'very much pleased with Longfellow's poems – excuse the writing for I am in an awkward position not sitting nor lying but doubled up in my bunk with the pasteboard for a desk. "Pursuit o' knowledge under difficulties".' The same individual concludes with the following piece of advice:

I wish to impress upon you the necessity of coming in the first cabin where there seems to be every comfort that can be had on board a ship. There are some reading others writing others card playing in a beautiful cabin beautifully lighted and here am I writing ... by a dingy lamp which gives light to write by and no more and so you must excuse my mistakes.[40]

In contrast to the grim situation between decks, the accommodation enjoyed by the first-class passenger in the mid-nineteenth century was a world away. As one authority observed in 1843, the saloon was 'a paradise when compared to the other parts of the ship'.[41] As competition became ever more fierce, the degree of comfort afforded the wealthy customer became a point of pride between shipping companies. With the arrival of clipper class ships every requirement imaginable was provided for the passenger who could pay the price. One of the most famous clippers of the time, the 'Red Jacket', carried 26 saloon passengers along with a gold cargo worth over £200,000 between Melbourne and Liverpool in May 1855. One anonymous traveller described the accommodation in his personal diary:

The After Saloon where I am is fitted up like a L'pool & Clyde Steamer the doors &c all finished wt. Mahogany & Rose & Satinwoods wt. gilded moldings & pilasters & has a library of 200 vols. forming a fair selection. There are couches & easy chairs & every thing like a drawing room.[42]

Before departure, many first-class passengers would have cabins fitted out to their own specifications. In most cases, this would involve the arrangement of furniture and belongings to best and economic effect in the personal cabin. Where this was not possible, carpenters could be hired at the docks to make 'ship shape' cabinets and tables for use at sea. While awaiting their passage for Australia in 1849, David and Mary McConell spent several days making their large cabin 'most comfortable', commissioning a carpenter to fit ample bookshelves and two swinging candle lamps which gave 'fair light'.[43] Where the arrangement of the cabin continued to be unsatisfactory, adjustments could be made along the way. Dr Arthur McKenzie was given the exclusive use of a double cabin, affording the use of a large table and two wall mounted cases, one containing books for recreational reading, the other a 'case of instruments – a row of medical and surgical books, my flute & mouth organ & hairbrush &c.' Although this proved a more than adequate situation in the daytime, the lighting arrangements he eventually found inadequate for nighttime reading. Several days into the voyage, McKenzie arranged for the ship's carpenter to put a 'fixed swing candle ... near head of bed so that I can read in bed', and before long overseeing the installation of 'a saloon reading lamp to read & write by at my desk'.[44]

The supplies of books that cabin passengers took to stave off the boredom of the voyage varied, though there was here to be found on most ships a marked contrast to the scarcity of reading matter found in corresponding steerage quarters.[45] Yet the mere availability of texts is not necessarily an indication of vigorous reading activity. Even where books were readily available, the intensity of their use could vary enormously from individual to individual. Contemplating the different attitudes of his fellow passengers on board the 'North Briton' in 1837, Revd William Hamilton observed:

Our passengers may be divided into three classes. Ones who depend for their happiness on eating & drinking card playing & jesting & the examination & exhibition of their various goods & chattels. These seem sometimes to feel life irksome & are often distressed with the length of interval from breakfast till dinner. They are however not destitute of good manners or wanting in civility. A second class have a more refined taste but want habits of reading & patient application to study. They turn from their books to their gun from their gun to their fishing tackle, & from these to their spie glasses & sextants. Then they betake themselves to light goodnatured conversation to trials of dexterity in climbing &c. Finally they return to their books & seem to find them agreeable for a short time. The third class is the most sedate and serious. They may be found for three or four hours daily walking the deck & enjoying conversation & as many hours engaged in observing the wonders of the deep. The rest of their time they are occupied in study either with or without the pen but at any rate in private.[46]

While the more studious passenger might spend most of his waking hours immersed in reading, others could be less inclined, regarding books as an expedient means of diversion when there was nothing more exciting to be found. The general tedium of life at sea could also be punctuated by untimely distraction. Reflecting on his Australian voyage in 1831, John Henderson remarked that 'a ship is *not* the best place in the world for study or meditation. Some interruption is constantly occurring. No sooner have you laid your books out before you ... than a fellow-passenger puts his head down a skylight'.[47] The first thing Henry Evans did on boarding the 'Great Britain' at Liverpool in 1853 was to put up his bookshelves. Conditions appear to have been near ideal for reading: he takes breakfast in bed, spends time in a centrally heated After Saloon, and in general finds 'time ... very hard to kill'. Yet it is a full fortnight before he opens his first book and, apart from several attempts at a collection of sermons, *Pickwick*, and a Scott novel, he appears not to have completed one volume throughout the voyage.[48] Another uncommitted reader was Francis Gosling who, on his way to Sydney on board the 'Alexander' in 1835, retired to his cabin every sabbath in order to read one sermon a week from a copy of the *Sunday Library*, given to him by his father before departure. Gosling – for whom books were little more than a means of mortifying the flesh – appears to have appreciated socialising far more than reading, never opening a book from Monday to Saturday, preferring instead to spend his weeks playing cards with the ladies, smoking with the gentlemen, fishing, and catching birds.[49]

The far less sociable Revd Hamilton was himself a voracious reader who would no doubt have placed himself within his own 'sedate and serious class'. Among the several books that accompanied his voyage were *The Life and Times of Alexander Henderson*, *The Protestant*, *Elijah the Tishbite*, *History of the Reformation*, and Martin's *Australian Colonies*. Habituated to the comfort and solitude of his study, even he found it difficult to read in the privacy of his cabin, 'owing to its vicinity to the hold & the warm close air which exhales from it'. The Saloon he also found intolerable, because it was 'always half full of company where conversation interferes with one's abstraction'. Consequently, much of his time is spent in search of suitable places to read. At one stage, we find him climbing the mast 'for the purpose of reading in some degree of privacy', inadvertently dropping his volume into the sea on the way down.

A more sociable example of the 'sedate and serious' type is to be found in the case of an unidentified passenger bound for the gold diggings in 1853. An amateur bibliographer, he spent much of the journey compiling a commonplace list of 'Books met with on voyage', each entry including a transcription of the relevant title-page, price and publication details, and in some cases detailed notes on the content:

Pub 1840

Wilson's rod & gun – this Book Embraces shooting and fishing with a dissertation on salmon ... sketches of fish & scenery & flies – including list of Books on fishing & shooting.... At the end of the treatise on fishing is the list of fishing Books including Salmonia or the days of fly fishing by Sir Humphray Davy 12mo 1828 and Angler in Wales or days and nights of sportsmen yales & traditions by Captain Medwin 2 vols 8vo – plates London. Those who are curious in regard to different editions of the earlier works may consult a catalogue of Books on angling 8vo 1811 Pub G. McEllies of the British Museum & originally printed in British Bibliographer.

Thanks to such vigilance, we are left with a remarkably detailed record of the titles circulated in the ship's saloon, as well as a near comprehensive record of the author's own reading habits. Among the titles he personally owned and read were Mosman's *Australia Visited*, Schmidt's *German Tales*, and Fouqué's *Sir Elidoe* and *Nudine* in German. On 31 May he loaned his copy of Chambers's *The Rudiments of Geology* to a fellow male passenger. On 8 June, he borrowed from a married woman a copy of Tomkins's *Beauties of English Poetry*, Wilson's *Rod and Gun* being loaned to him on the 24th. On the second leg of the voyage from St Paul's to Hobson's Bay he was to lend to a young woman – mysteriously referred to as 'La Belle' – a copy of Longfellow's *Poems* and, shortly before arrival, we find him swapping a biography of the 'three Clarks' for a Danish edition of Lepon. Other books which he lists as having encountered on the way include Herschel's *Manual of Scientific Enquiry*, Dana's *Seaman's Manual*, Mitchell's *Planetary and Stellar System*, Lloyd's *Field Sports of Northern Europe*, Miller's *Scenes and Legends of the North of Scotland*, Chambers's *Scottish Songs* and *Scottish Ballads* in two volumes each, *Les Belles de Nuit*, *Sailing Directions*, Milligan's *The Passions; or, Mind and Matter*, *Treatise on Economic Currency*, Chambers's *Rudiments of Chemistry*, Revd Murray's *Pitcairn*, *Lectures on Gold for Instruction of Emigrants about to Proceed to Australia*, Burrow's *The Geography of Hudson's Bay*, Clark's *Elements of Drawing and Perspective*, Scoffira's *Gold Seekers Chemical Guide*, Michaud's *History of the Crusades*, Lawrence's *Lectures on the History of Man*.

While it is unlikely that this represents anything like a comprehensive list of the books owned by the cabin passengers on board – a distinctly masculine bias is detectable for instance – such an inventory at least allows us to speculate as to the kind of reading that might have been conducted on the 'Calphurnia' in 1853. In our diarist's own record, for instance, there is a clear commitment to reading as self-improvement. Although interrupted by the 'flickering & swinging of light', we find him in early July endeavouring to teach himself German and geology. There is also detectable in the choice of texts a strong reliance on the connection between enquiry and survival, more than evident in the emphasis on the natural sciences. And, finally, there are potential elements of cultural nostalgia detectable in the use so far from home of familiar poetry and song.

One of the most important functions of reading, as more than one passenger was to discover, was as a means of protection against others. John Hood observed on his way to New South Wales in 1843 that he and his fellow travellers were 'as yet on our good behaviour, and cautious and wary as to whom we shall enter into friendly intercourse with.... Like people in a crowded omnibus ... our books and journals are our resources.' Later in the voyage Hood was still to be found in his cabin, spending most of his time reading and writing, after dinner returning to his solitude, 'preferring my books to the coteries'.[50] Elizabeth Monaghan, too, remarked on how grateful she was for the arrival of inclement weather, not least because of the reprieve it brought from the undesired company of deck society: 'I can be ... so much more alone, get a book & shut myself up in my cabin quite cosy.'[51] These and other remarks indicate the symbolic importance of the book as a means of preserving private space. As one authority informed his readers:

When the cushions at the after part of the saloon are arranged in a particularly inviting manner and a book or glove is placed thereon, it may be surmised that the occupant of the couch is absent temporarily and if another were to take possession it would be an intrusion.[52]

While it has been argued that reading is by nature a distinctly anti-social activity, there is evidence to suggest that the use of books at sea could serve important social functions, even in some cases reinforcing a sense of common identity. One of the most popular shipboard entertainments in the nineteenth century was reading aloud. In 1859, chapters from *Pickwick* were nightly read out after dinner on the 'La Hogue', for instance, while in the mornings the female passengers read to each other sections of *Sketches by Boz*. Texts could also become public property through their frequent borrowing and lending. An important symbolic act, the lending of a book could provide a welcome opportunity for meaningful exchange between strangers. The enjoyment of the same text often engendered a sense of mutuality, even intimacy, between readers, and books were frequently given on the voyage as tokens of friendship. On occasion such gifts could even act as a prelude to courtship between the sexes. We know that on board the 'La Hogue', at least one young woman was given permission by Mr Jilks – elsewhere described as 'an old batchelor' – 'to enter his cabin to take any book she may find there'.[53]

For the cabin passenger, the Saloon was the main focus of social life, a place for public entertainment, religious observances, and the exchange of information. In the potentially tense atmosphere that could surround a small community thrown together in relatively confined quarters, overt sociability was officially encouraged, most obviously through the regular organisation of amateur theatricals and concerts. By mid-century one of the more popular saloon entertainments was the circulation of manuscripts in the form of newspapers, many examples of which survive, most usually in versions printed by subscription after arrival as mementoes of the voyage. So popular was the production of shipboard newspapers to become that the editor of one could refer to it in 1869 as 'quite an institution ... on the route between Australia and the Mother Country'.[54]

Although they tended to be more entertaining than serious – most are a light-hearted combination of facetious wit, humorous observation, and general knowledge – their very existence suggests something about the importance of texts to the maintenance of shipboard society. Usually circulated on a weekly basis in one or two manuscript copies to be consulted in a public place, one of the explicit aims of the shipboard newspaper was to engender civility among passengers. As the prospectus of one put it in 1879:

The *Aconcagua Times* is undertaken at the request of our fellow-passengers to be a Journal of our floating commonwealth. Its politics, its principles will be strictly Conservative. It will support by its influence, the government, the discipline, the good order of the organised society in which for six weeks we are here to live.[55]

Given the close proximity in which these passengers were living, eating, and sleeping, the domesticity of the situation was often remarked upon. The publication of comic journals within families had been common from the eighteenth century, and so in a sense these texts were an extension of an already existing cultural practice. Yet these were not family members but strangers, for whom the preservation of a modest distance was important to the maintenance of private life. Shipboard newspapers, in their mimicry of the public sphere, allowed for a tangible expression of sociability while still creating a rhetorical distance between those involved in their production and circulation.

Perhaps, more importantly, the very existence of such documents indicates the extent to which a contemporary press had become by the mid-nineteenth century a necessity for the organisation of social life. This was never truer than in a colonial context, according to Benedict Anderson, who argues that the imagination of cultural synchronicity across vast distances was to a great extent made possible in the nineteenth century through the mediation of print:

It became conceivable to dwell on the Peruvian altiplano, on the Pampas of Argentina, or the harbours of 'New' England, and yet feel connected to certain regions or communities, thousands of miles away, in England or on the Iberian peninsula. One could be fully aware of a shared language and a religious faith (to varying degrees), customs and traditions, without any great expectation of meeting one's partners.[56]

The thousands of books, tracts, letters, and newspapers that made their way to the colonies in the nineteenth century provided vital connections with familiar social values, serving for many to organise an otherwise unpredictable environment into recognisable patterns under strange skies. By the end of the century reading had become for thousands of seaborne passengers a practical necessity, the profundity of three months in cultural isolation engendering for many the most intense relationship that they would ever have with the printed word.

References

The research for this paper would not have been possible without the generous support of the Carnegie Trust and the Humanities Research Centre at the Australian National University.

1.   As *The Emigrant's Friend* advised its readers in 1852, 'the voyage on which you are entering is a long one' necessitating that books become 'the companion of your days and nights' [*The Emigrant's Friend: Being a Companion for the Voyage and a Manual of Instruction in his New Home* (London: Religious Tract Society, 1852), p.4]. The aptly named *Voyage Companion: A Parting Gift to Female Emigrants* [(London: Gilpin, 1850), p.35] also exhorted, 'Let me make good books my companions as often as I can do so.... Good books are like good friends. We never tire of them, and daily grow the better for their acquaintance.' Where 'there is not much room to walk about on a ship's deck', remarked another authority in 1854, 'the only thing is to sit still'. In such a situation 'reading is a never-failing amusement'. *Remarks for the Use of Emigrants*, Emigrant Tract XI (London: SPCK, 1854), p.9.

2.   Revd David McKenzie, *Ten Years in Australia* (London: William Orr, 1851), pp.152–3.

3.   John Mathison, *Counsel for Emigrants and Interesting Information* (Aberdeen: Mathison, 1834), p.x.

4.   *Chambers's Edinburgh Journal*, no.1, (4 February 1832), pp.1–2. Other periodicals tailored specifically to the needs of the prospective emigrant included *The Emigrants' Penny Magazine*, established in April 1850 'to promote the spread of information at home and abroad, and to afford instruction and amusement to the class for which they are especially intended' [*The Emigrants' Penny Magazine*, 1:2 (June 1850), p.28]. More practical than entertaining, the magazine served as the official organ of the British Ladies' Female Emigrant Society.

5.   P. B. Chadfield, *Out at Sea; or, The Emigrant Afloat* (Derby: Chadfield, n.d.).

6.   Advertisement bound in with *The Sunday-School Boy in Australia*, Emigrant Tract XIII (SPCK, 1851).

7.   One of the earliest examples is an extensive emigrants' library distributed by the Society for Promoting Christian Knowledge in 1839, 'consisting of works selected

from the Catalogues of the Society'. *An Account of the Origin, Objects, and General Proceedings of the Society for Promoting Christian Knowledge* (London: SPCK, 1839), p.37.

8.   Advertisement in *The Emigrants' Penny Magazine*, 1:4 (August 1850), n.p.

9.   William Stones, *New Zealand: The Land of Promise and its Resources*, 7th edn (London: Shaw, Savill & Co., 1864), p.89.

10. Sidney Smith, *The Settler's New Home; or The Emigrant's Location, being a Guide to Emigrants in the Selection of a Settlement, and the Preliminary Details of the Voyage* (London: Kendrick, 1849), p.ii.

11. David McKenzie, *Ten Years in Australia*, pp.152–3.

12. Quoted Mathison, p.107.

13. Revd Aeneas MacKenzie, *The Emigrant's Guide to Australia* (London: Clark, Beeton & Co., 1853), p.180.

14. Although 'it was uncommon to find a home which lacked any literature', remarks Vincent, 'the size and scope of the cottage libraries were usually extremely limited.' David Vincent, *Literacy and Popular Culture: England 1750–1914* (Cambridge: Cambridge University Press, 1993), p.110.

15. *Emigrants' Penny Magazine*, 1:4 (August 1850), p.161.

16. *Preparations for the Voyage*, (London: SPCK, 1851), p.46.

17. *A Letter to Young Female Emigrants* (London: SPCK, 1850), p.2.

18. *The Voyage Companion: A Parting Gift to Female Emigrants* (London: Charles Gilpin, 1850), p.22.

19. *The Emigrant's Friend; Or, Scriptural Instruction for a Long Voyage* (Montrose: published for the author, 1851), n.p.

20. *Emigrants' Penny Magazine*, 1:4 (August 1850), p.133.

21. William Johnston, London to Launceston, per 'Arab', 1841–2 [quoted in Don Charlwood, *The Long Farewell* (Warrandyte: Burgewood, 1981), pp.109–10].

22. See Richard Altick, *The English Common Reader*, p.91.

23. John Mackenzie, Diary on a passage to Port Philip (1841) [National Library of Australia MS 685].

24. P. B. Chadfield, *Out at Sea; Or, The Emigrant Afloat* (Derby: Chadfield, n.d.), p.12.

25. Basil Greenhill and Ann Giffard, *Travelling by Sea in the Nineteenth Century: Interior Design in Victorian Passenger Ships* (London: A&C Black, 1972, p.23.

26. William Nichols, Diary from London–Sydney, per 'James Gibb' (1849) [NLA MS 8166].

27. Elizabeth Britton, Plymouth to Melbourne, per 'Hereford', 1853 [Australian National Maritime Museum MS HER].

28. Samuel Sidney, p.109.

29. [Alexander Turnbull Library (Wellington, NZ) MS 89.049].

30. Isabella Ritchie, Diary on board the 'Henderson', 1863 [ATL MS 88–222].

31. Richard Altick, pp.107, 104.

32. Quoted in Andrew Hassam, *No Privacy for Writing* (Melbourne University Press, 1995), p.214.

33. Revd John Jennings Smith, Plymouth to Sydney, per 'Amelia', 1839 [ANMM MS AME]; Revd John Davies Mereweather, *Life on Board an Emigrant Ship: Being a Diary of a Voyage to Australia* (London: Hatchard, 1852), p.18.

34. John Murray, Diary [ATL MS 89.1843].

35. Thomas McCombie, *Essays on Colonization* (London: Smith and Elder, 1850), p.116.

36. J. D. Forbes, Diary per 'Guildford', bound for Sydney, 1827 [NLA MS 7565].
37. Charles Bateson, *The Convict Ships* (Glasgow: Brown, Son, and Ferguson, 1969), pp.308–9.
38. *Voices of Our Exiles*, 1 (13 February, 1864) [NLA MS 6037].
39. Quoted in *Life in a Young Colony: Selections from Early New Zealand Writing*, ed. Cherry A. Hankin (Christchurch: Whitcoulls, 1981), pp.30–40.
40. Diary of George Burnett ['Batten down the hatch'] London to Auckland, per 'Victory' (1850–1) [ATL (Wellington, NZ) MS 89–364].
41. John Hood, *Australia and the East: A Journal of a Voyage to New South Wales* (London: John Murray, 1843).
42. Anon diary, Melbourne to Liverpool, per 'Red Jacket', 1855 [ANMM MS RED].
43. Mary McConnell, *Memories of Days Long Gone* (n.p., 1909), p.6.
44. Dr Arthur Colin McKenzie, Diary of a voyage from England to Rockhampton, per 'Merkara' (1890) [ANMM MS MER].
45. Cabin conditions were often comparatively comfortable enough to prompt acts of kindness towards the less fortunate. Sensing the need, passengers on board the 'Norfolk' in 1862 freely supplied the minister with a collection of popular publications, among them *Sunday at Home*, *The Family Treasury*, and *The Leisure Hour*, for free distribution in steerage. [Diary of Revd Frederick Miller, Melbourne to London, per 'Norfolk' (1861–2) [ANMM MS NOR]].
46. Diary of Revd William Hamilton, Leith to Hobart, per 'North Briton' (1837) [NLA MS 2117].
47. John Henderson, *Excursions and Adventures in New South Wales* (London: 1851), p.163.
48. Diary of Henry Vaughan Evans, Liverpool to Sydney, per 'Great Britain', 1854 [ANMM MS GRE].
49. Diary of Francis Gosling, London to Sydney, per 'Alexander', 1835 [ANMM MS ALE].
50. John Hood, *Australia and the East: A Narrative of a Voyage to New South Wales* (London: John Murray, 1843), pp.9, 31.
51. Monaghan [ANMM MS QUE].
52. 'Notice', 'The Capstan Head' [NLA MS 2108].
53. Diary of James Hogg Swain, Greenwick to Sydney, per 'La Hogue' (1859) [ANMM MS LA].
54. 'Introduction', *Lady Jocelyn Weekly Mail* (London: Haddon, 1869), n.p. Among the texts circulated on board the 'Lady Jocelyn' that same year were copies of at least three newspapers produced on other voyages 'and printed for general circulation on arrival'.
55. *The Aconcagua Times* (Edinburgh: Ballantyne, 1879), p.3.
56. Benedict Anderson, *Imagined Communities: Reflections on the Origin and Spread of Nationalism* (London: Verso, 1991), p.72.

The information resources of the Royal Geographical Society (with the Institute of British Geographers)

ANDREW TATHAM

THE FOUNDATION OF THE Royal Geographical Society in 1830 marked a coming of age of geographical enquiry. The retelling of travellers' tales at a dining club was replaced by a more prosaic approach. As the Society's objectives expressed it, the purpose was 'to collect, register, and digest, and to print, … such new, interesting, and useful facts and discoveries'. The new Society went further, and before the end of the year, the first constitution had specified that 'the Society shall also commence the formation of a Library, with a collection of Maps and instruments connected with Geographical Science'. In this focus on Geographical Science, the founding fathers of the Society were consciously adopting the mood of the time. Recent arrivals on the London scene included the Geological Society (1807), the Royal Astronomical Society (1820) and the Zoological Society (1828), while in Paris and Berlin, Geographical Societies had been founded in 1821 and 1828 respectively.

In these early days, another significant formative attitude was expressed by Barrow, in the Memorandum he submitted to the meeting of the Raleigh Club in May 1830, which is generally taken to be the foundation event of the Society. Barrow suggested, as the second of the objects proposed for the Society that it should '… accumulate gradually a library of the best books on geography – a complete collection of maps and charts from the earliest period of rude geographical delineations to the most improved of the present time; as well as all such documents and materials as may convey the best information to persons intending to visit foreign countries …'.

Through the liberality of its fellows and other donors, both individual and corporate, the Society has been able to fulfil the ideals of the founders to the extent that the holdings today are both substantial and unparalleled as a resource of geographical information. As such, they make a significant contribution to the national heritage as well as to our understanding of the world and its peoples and environments. To demonstrate this, there follow five case studies. Each approaches the holdings in a different way, which is indicative of the variety of use and interest in the collections. Each could be replaced by many more – the case studies represent but the snowflake on top of the tip of the iceberg.

Livingstone

A missionary who fought the slave trade, an explorer who contributed to Western understanding of the African Great Lakes region, an imperialist whose name is still revered in East Africa; David Livingstone is, without doubt an iconic figure in the history of the nineteenth century. The Society's holdings span all of these histories to the extent that in the National Portrait Gallery's major exhibition on Livingstone in 1996, 20% of the items displayed were from the Society's collections. Artefacts, such as his prismatic compass or sextant, published books and pamphlets, maps and lithographs, stand alongside his original manuscript drawings, maps and letters, and sketches, paintings and photographs of Livingstone and those who travelled with him. While items such as the slave chains bring the reality of the slave trade to life, Baines's painting from the Zambesi expedition of the Kebrasa Falls with a photographer in the foreground marks the changing technologies available to record the places visited. Similarly, following a sequence through the holdings from Livingstone's manuscript map of, for example, the shore-line of Lake Nyasa (now Malawi) through a draughtsman's compilation to the published work illustrates both the process of his discovery and the process of carto-graphic production – a method of working which is now entirely superseded.

History through photography

Although the Society's foundation predates the invention of photography by less than a decade, it was rather longer before the camera became a regular part of an expedition's equipment. Indeed, not until 1884 did the Society's Council authorise the regular collection of photography to supplement the maps, reports, paintings and sketches and bring another element to the geographical record. As with the older collections, earlier material was soon donated, including Sir John Kirk's photographs of Zanzibar from 1862–3. From that time to the present, photography has undergone almost continuous technological revolution, and the Society's holdings provide a significant longitudinal study of this process. At the same time, they illuminate not only the photographer's subject in the view finder, but also the subjectivity of the photographer and his or her preconceptions. Nonetheless, as the recent collaboration with the British Council over an exhibition of Sir H. H. Johnstone's Caribbean photographs has shown, the cultural heritage of peoples and places that are frequently changed beyond all recognition by the 50 or 100 intervening years is wonderfully illustrated by the Society's holdings.

OS County Series (six inch)
This scale of detailed topographical mapping was begun by the Ordnance Survey in Ireland, and from there was extended to the rest of the United Kingdom, commencing in 1840. Ten years after the opening of the Map Room to the general public at the time of the Crimean War in 1854, the Ordnance Survey decided to deposit copies of its products for public use. These included the County Series and the deposit at this scale, or its metric equivalent, has continued to the recent demise of paper mapping products at this scale, but with a few gaps. Although there is no complete collection of this series anywhere, the Ordnance Survey's own holdings being severely damaged by the Southampton blitz, the Society is a very good starting point for anyone using the series.

Everest
The search for and the ascent of the world's highest mountain was a challenge which engaged many from the late eighteenth century until the first successful ascent in 1953. Since then the mountain has remained a magnet to climber and, increasingly, to tourists. The Society has played a key role in this process, and in the wider growth of knowledge about the geography of the whole of the central Asian area. In the latter part of the last century, it was here that the 'great game' was played out, with significant advances in geographical knowledge being made by the pundits, by British reconnaissance officers, by the Survey of India, and by geographers from both Britain and Russia. Much of this was recorded in the Society's journals, and manuscript accounts of many expeditions are held in the Archives. Here too are the archives of the Mount Everest Committee (later the Mount Everest Foundation) which planned the attempted ascents of Everest from 1921 onwards. Illustrations from these climbs, equipment used and books or reports published are all part of the Society's heritage resources. A further resource is the series of maps of the Mount Everest area, drawn from accumulated information, by the Society's cartographers.

Guide books

It was noted above that one of the stated purposes of the Library was to '... accumulate ... such documents and materials as may convey the best information to persons intending to visit foreign countries ...' It is not surprising therefore that the Society's Library holds what may well be the finest collection of guide books in the world. From the 1850s and 1860s to the present day, many publishers of guide books, like Karl Baedeker of Cologne, Hachette of Paris, and John Murray of London, and their successors such as Lonely Planet, Footprint and others, have deposited copies of their work in the Society's Library. These now form an extremely important research resource on the changing geography of the towns and countries covered, as well as a unique source of raw material in the history of the geography of tourism. Alongside the standard popular series, the Society holds more specialised series, such as the Admiralty Handbooks and Pilots, the works of the English Place-name Society, and gazetteers from the eighteenth century onwards. These are complemented by maps and, from the 1860s, photographs of many of the localities concerned. The earlier history of the guide book is not forgotten either, and is well served by the remarkable collection donated to the Society by Sir George Fordham in 1923 of guide books, road-books and maps from the seventeenth, eighteenth and nineteenth centuries.

The future

While the earliest items date from the 1480s, the Society's holdings are certainly not simply an historic collection. New materials are being added every day, enlarging our understanding of the geography of the world in which we live. Our challenge for the future is to make all these items, old and new, and the geographical information they contain, available to those who need them, whether in formal education or life-long learning. The Society's project 'Unlocking the Archives' seeks to do this through creating a single electronic catalogue of all the materials, concentrating on the rarer and older materials in the first instance, through creating a new unified storage and readers' area, and through developing a range of services for education including curriculum-based materials and programmes. We look forward to an exciting new stage in the history of the Society and its information resources.

Bibliography

Archer-Straw, P., 1998: *Photos and Phantasms – Harry Johnston's photographs of the Caribbean*, London: The British Council.

Baedeker's handbooks for travellers, a bibliography of English editions published prior to World War 2, Westport, Conn: Greenwood Press.

Cameron, I.,1980: *To the farthest ends of the earth*, London: Macdonald.

Clark, P. K., 1986: *The Map Collector* 35, pp.2–7 'A useful collection of maps and charts'.

Crone, G. R., 1953: *J. Inst. Navigation* 6, pp.38–43 'Early books and charts in the Royal Geographical Society's collection'.

Crone, G. R., 1955: *GJ* 121, pp.27–32 *The Library of the Royal Geographical Society*.

Crone, G. R. & Day, E. E. T., 1960: *GJ* 126, pp.12–17 *The Map Room of the Royal Geographical Society*.

Freeman, M. J. & Longbotham, J., 1981: *The Fordham Collection – A catalogue* (Historical Geography Research Series, No.5) Norwich: GeoAbstracts Ltd.

MacKenzie, J. M. (ed.), 1996: *David Livingstone and the Victorian encounter with Africa*, London: National Portrait Gallery.

Mill, H. R., 1930: *The record of the Royal Geographical Society 1830–1930*, London: The Society.

Ryan, R. R., 1997: *Picturing Empire – Photography and the visualization of the British Empire*, London: Reaktion Books.

Index